DEADLY
SECRETS

Karen Scalf Linamen
and Keith A. Wall

NAVPRESS ®
A MINISTRY OF THE NAVIGATORS
P.O. BOX 6000, COLORADO SPRINGS, COLORADO 80934

The Navigators is an international Christian organization. Jesus Christ gave His followers the Great Commission to go and make disciples (Matthew 28:19). The aim of The Navigators is to help fulfill that commission by multiplying laborers for Christ in every nation.

NavPress is the publishing ministry of The Navigators. NavPress publications are tools to help Christians grow. Although publications alone cannot make disciples or change lives, they can help believers learn biblical discipleship, and apply what they learn to their lives and ministries.

© 1990 by Karen Linamen and Keith Wall
All rights reserved, including translation
Library of Congress Catalog Card Number.
    90-61786
ISBN 08910-93206

All Scripture in this publication is from the *Holy Bible: New International Version* (NIV). Copyright © 1973, 1978, 1984, International Bible Society. Used by permission of Zondervan Bible Publishers.

Printed in the United States of America

Contents

IN APPRECIATION

*Our sincerest appreciation is due to
the Cameron family and Scott's close friends.
Often at great personal cost,
these individuals were willing to
relive and recount the events in this book
so that Scott's story could be told.*

Karen dedicates her work on this book to the
memory of her cousin Michael Gene Panknin,
July 16, 1955 to February 23, 1987.

At the time Karen first learned about Scott Cameron and his family, Michael was just weeks away from his own AIDS-induced death. He died shortly after recommitting his heart and soul to the God who knows our deepest secrets . . . and loves us still.

Authors

Karen Scalf Linamen is a freelance writer and author or co-author of four books, including: *The Curious Waltz of the Working Woman: Finding Your Personal Rhythm in the Dance Between Family, Work and Friends.*

Keith A. Wall is a magazine editor for Focus on the Family in Pomona, California. He is also a freelance writer and author of numerous magazine articles.

About This Book

This is a true story, based on the journals of one young man who lived a harrowing journey from darkness to light, from loneliness to love, from secrecy to sharing.

Scott Cameron left a legacy of more than a dozen journals, spanning nearly fifteen years: three-inch-thick school binders brimming with literally thousands of pages covered front and back. His entries were often typed.

From these detailed accounts, events and entire conversations have been reconstructed. Interviews with family and friends have filled in the gaps even further. In *Deadly Secrets*, journal entries appear as excerpts, and also as Scott's thoughts, which are indicated in italic type throughout the manuscript.

Scott's exact words reflect his struggles and his triumphs, his darkest secrets and his search for wholeness. The result? A portrayal that is as accurate as it is fast-moving and dramatic.

To protect the privacy of family and friends, names have been changed, as have identifying details. Some of the characters are composites of the many people who played parts in the drama of Scott's life.

It is our hope, and the hope of Scott's courageous family, that his story might encourage Christians everywhere regardless of the name of the dark secret with which they struggle: adultery . . . substance abuse . . . homosexuality . . . abortion . . . or a festering wound from an event of the past—rape, molestation, bereavement, betrayal.

In the final analysis, we all hurt, don't we? We all have sins, we all have wounds. Yet perhaps that's the very thing that draws us closer to each other as well as to God, as we reach out from hearts that know firsthand what it's like to hurt and lift one another in prayer to our Lord Jesus Christ, who bears scars of His own.

ONE

On a Crash-and-Burn Course

J ust after noon on a slightly overcast day in July 1985, Scott Cameron sat in his Mustang, staring silently past a couple of ten-year-old boys skateboarding on the sidewalk of the quiet, tree-lined street where he grew up.

God, was I ever that young? That free? His brows knit at the thought. He wiped away a bead of sweat trickling from his hairline, then leaned to unroll a window even though the car was still cool from the air conditioner.

Five minutes passed. Then ten. Scott eyed the brick and green-stucco house across the street. If he waited much longer, someone might glance out through the '70s-style beads that hung like curtains across the kitchen window facing the street.

He brushed back a lock of auburn hair with hands that shook more than just a little. He grasped the door handle, took a last deep breath, and climbed from his sanctuary. The slam of the car door behind him seemed exaggerated and echoed in his head all the way across the sidewalk and up the porch steps. His mouth felt like cotton, his fingers like Jell-O. Still, he managed to grip the doorknob.

It felt like a slow motion scene in some big-screen movie. In fact, one came to mind: *The Silver Streak* with Gene Wilder. A runaway train, heading into the station at about a million miles an hour, simply couldn't be stopped. Suddenly cameras downshifted to slow motion. Train met building. Bricks flew. Glass shattered and sprayed. Bystanders dove for safety. Twisting metal screamed. There was a kind of heart-stopping grace about the demolition, slowed to a tortuous crawl at the cue of a director.

But this wasn't a movie.

This was real life, and the collision had already been set into motion. Scott Cameron was on a crash-and-burn course.

Scott opened the front door.

A thin man with chiseled features sat reading the Saturday paper on an avocado-green couch. He looked up, surprised, then broke into a grin. "Gail!" he hollered toward the kitchen, "Scotty's here." Chuck Cameron struggled to his feet, then crossed the small living room toward his son, moving with a rhythmic, labored gait earned from a twenty-five-year battle with arthritis.

Gail Cameron, tiny, bright, and energetic, bubbled in from the adjacent kitchen, flashing an electric smile. "Hi, sweetie. I have stuffed grape leaves in the oven." She approached Scott for the traditional squeeze and kiss. "I called to tell you, but you weren't home. Out with Lauren? You *can* stay for dinner, right? Scott? *Scott?* You okay, honey?"

Scott moved for the first time since entering the house. He nodded briefly. "Sure. Sure, Mom."

Gail herded her family toward the heart of the home—the formica-topped kitchen table where they had gathered thousands of times before, sharing meals, games, conversations, cookies and milk. Gail had pinned the kids' Halloween costumes atop this well-scarred table. Scott had done his homework there a thousand times. Scott slid into "his" chair without a thought for the memories. He had no room for memories right now. His terror was too great.

There was some small talk. Something about Scott's college classes and his job at the hospital and whether or not there was enough wholesome food in the refrigerator at his bachelor apartment. The words whizzed by Scott's head at phenomenal speed. Or maybe Scott was the one speeding, and the words were standing still. Yes, that was it. Someone was flinging small talk at the pounding dark mass of a runaway train.

Scott's chair scraped against the linoleum as he stood to his feet. He almost heard the hiss and screech of the steam-powered brakes. But it was too late to stop the crash.

"Mom, Dad, there's bad news." He felt the weighted impact of every word as time slammed to a halt. "I'm . . . I'm sick. . . ."

"Sick?" Gail echoed. "I hope you don't have that flu they've been talking about on the news."

"No, Mom. It's not the flu. It's something . . . something worse than that."

"Worse?"

"A lot worse. It's . . . it's something you may not have heard about yet. It's called AIDS."

Chuck furrowed his brow. "AIDS? How bad is that, son?"

"Sweetie, is it something from the hospital? From one of the patients?"

Scott squeezed his eyes closed. His fists clenched. "Real bad. And no, it's not from the hospital." His heart pounded a deafening rhythm in his ears. "It's . . . it's a *gay* disease."

Gail looked puzzled. "Honey, there must have been *someone,* maybe someone from school. . . ."

"No! Oh, God, Mom . . . it's *not* from the hospital. And it's not from my school. Dad, Mom, I'm . . . I'm homosexual. I have AIDS. I'm *dying.*"

Hours later, back in his apartment across town, Scott slumped on the floor in his bedroom, his back against the wall. His eyes were rimmed with red. Staring blankly into space, he remembered his mother's tears. Gail had clung to him as if he were a child, despite the fact that he towered over her head by a foot or more. Chuck, stunned, had sat silent at the little formica table. And then he had wept.

They'd never even suspected their son was gay.

They thought he was happily dating and that he might marry

a young woman named Lauren. There had been no signs of inner struggle. Scott had been the life of every party from junior high to college. Active in church, he had loved God from boyhood. In fact, his parents had dedicated Scott to God long before, as Gail and Chuck had prayed for four years for a child the doctors said they had little chance of conceiving. On the day Gail had discovered she was pregnant with their firstborn, the tests confirmed something her body had been telling her for weeks and her heart had desired for years. She had long prayed for a son—a red-haired son. And for years she had known what she would name him.

Scott was the son she had known and loved before conception. And then one sultry summer afternoon she found out she hardly knew him at all. Scott had kept a dark secret from them all. And now it was going to kill him.

Still crumpled against the wall, Scott shook his head. But the thoughts in it remained painfully lodged. A single tear threatened to trace a path down his rugged face.

He wiped his eyes with the back of his hand, then scanned the bedroom. The room brimmed with all the little personal things that say so much about a life. There were photo albums, awards, and letters and a comic book collection that numbered in the thousands. From a framed five-by-seven photo on the dresser, the pixie-face of his younger sister, Tammy, flashed an innocent smile.

And then there were his journals. Fourteen years of journals, to be precise. A junior high teacher, long, long ago, had doled out the assignment of keeping a journal for a year. That started the flow. Now, a dozen or so overflowing notebooks gathered dust in a flat box under his bed. Scott had been trying something new, and his latest entries were stored on his Macintosh computer. But at that moment he reached for the cardboard box.

He picked out a small green diary—the five-and-dime-store kind that fastens with a little metal lock and a couple of miniature aluminum keys. Its binding was broken, and the loose pages that fell to the floor were dog-eared and covered with the childish print-scrawl of a twelve-year-old boy. The ink had already begun to fade. Scott folded himself cross-legged on the floor, pushed back a lock of hair, and fingered the cracked cover of the time-worn little book.

He touched a second book. Smoothed the wrinkled pages of a third. Finally, he reached for a green three-ring binder that showed the wear and tear of a decade. The year 1975 was scrawled in black marker on its cover. And in the lower left corner, a faded "Jesus Loves You" sticker curled at the edges.

Outside the tiny apartment, a dying sun painted the sky. Somewhere in the summer twilight children's voices rang. A little further away, a car door slammed faintly, and a woman's voice summoned someone home to dinner.

But the summer sounds fell on deaf ears. Scott was staring down at the pages of the diary, where the words danced and blurred as he blinked back the tears, and the memories that accompanied them were thick in the dusky light filtering in through the window.

TWO

This Close to Love

"**P**ssst." A freckled girl in blue jeans and a sweat shirt leaned precariously out of her seat. She shot a furtive glance at the teacher. Luckily, his back was still turned as he chalked out the date on the blackboard: Friday, May 20, 1975. Only one week left at Liberty High. The girl hissed again at a pair of shoulders across the aisle and two seats ahead. "*Pssssst! Cameron!*"

Scott turned around in time to see a crumpled note shoot across the gray linoleum and lodge beneath the gym bag at his feet. He dropped a pencil and retrieved the note. He opened it with as little noise as possible, smoothing the page in his lap, then slid it onto the desk and into his open textbook.

Scott—

You've got to promise not to tell if I tell you something. I'm only telling you because you're like a brother to me.

I guess I'm sort of in love with this guy from church. I really like him! The problem is, he's twelve years older than me. Do you think a thirty-year-old would ever go out with a high school senior?

I know it's a stupid problem. I haven't told anyone. But I knew I could tell you. You're such a pal. Just like a brother. And you're always willing to listen to all my guy-problems. Anyway, think about it, then write me back. Leave a note in my locker, okay?

Love, Melanie

Scott nodded back to Melanie, then faced the teacher again. He picked up his pencil. But his mind wasn't on the lecture. A few minutes later, Scott reread Melanie's note, a single phrase sticking in his brain like a burr: *Just like a brother. . . . Just like a brother. . . . Just like a brother.*

Scott leaned back in his chair, folded his arms across his chest and stared out the window. A week ago, hearing that old familiar line would have made him cringe. But not today. Today things were different. A slow smile formed on his lips.

Minutes passed and the smile remained intact.

The bell startled Scott out of his reverie. He scooped up the letter, books, and gym bag and exited the classroom in a stream of jostling students. Outside, a bustling lunchtime crowd filled the hallway. Girls applied lipstick by mirrors glued inside locker doors. Freshmen jockeyed in line for the drinking fountain. A couple leaned, lip-locked, against the trophy case, her arms around his waist, his hands tucked inside the back pockets of her designer jeans.

There was an excitement in the air, and not just because it was Friday. Above it all, snatches of dialogue buzzed through the hallways.

". . . and nobody asked her? I can't believe it!"

". . . got it back from the seamstress *yesterday.* After she promised it'd be done a week ago."

". . . taking *her?* What for? Is he hard up?"

". . . cool down some tonight. If it doesn't, I'll wilt in that dress."

Scott found a vacant bench in the Senior Square and sat down. He pulled a paper sack out of his gym bag, extracted a peanut butter and jelly sandwich, and winced down at the soggy purple bread. Several feet away, a cluster of fellow seniors lounged on the grass. They erupted in laughter and a blonde girl screamed as one of the guys held her lunch bag hostage.

"Hey, Scott. How you doing?" Paul Reardon plunked down on the bench next to Scott. The six-foot surfer, sporting collar length sun-blond hair, pulled a burger from the box lunch he had bought in the cafe. "You ready for the big event tonight?"

"Yep. Minus a few details. Washing the car, picking up the flowers. Things like that. And you?"

"Me too," Paul said through a mouthful.

"Who'd you finally decide to take?"

"Amanda Thornton."

"That's good."

"Yeah," Paul swallowed and flashed Scott a grin. "She's really cool. I think I really like her. A lot."

"Oh. Well . . . great." Scott's eyes darted away from Paul's. Scott stared at the ground a moment before continuing. "That's great, Paul. Really great."

Paul finished the burger and grabbed a couple of oatmeal cookies. "And what about you? You going with Melanie again?"

"Melanie? No way. We're just friends."

"That never bothered you before. What about Helen?"

Scott made a face. "C'mon Paul. This is the senior prom, remember? Gimme a break."

"Who then?"

Scott squared his shoulders and tried to hide a smile. "Wendy Dolen."

"Wendy Dolen?" Paul let out a low whistle. "Good for you! So what got you all inspired?"

Scott stood to go, crumpling his paper sack and tossing it easily into a nearby trash can. He reached for his books. The corner of a letter, half-tucked inside a textbook, caught his eye. *Just like a brother. . . . Just like a brother.*

Scott smiled. "I guess I'm just ready for a change."

The afternoon filled with a whirlwind of details as Scott picked up his tux and Wendy's corsage, washed the car, studied the map, and checked his wallet nine times to make sure his tickets were safe.

A half hour before it was time to pick up his date, Scott stood in front of the bathroom mirror—again—to recomb his hair. The wiry, auburn hair conspired against him, the most unmanageable at the most crucial times. He wet the comb and ran it through one more time, then stopped to study his reflection in the mirror.

He saw a lanky redhead with a winsome smile and a well-hidden zit on the left side of his face. *Thank God for Clearasil.* Scott leaned closer to the mirror. The eyes that stared back at him were piercing, searching. What would Wendy see when she looked at him? Someone cool? Someone nerdy? Someone lonely? And what did Scott see? Could even Scott see past the facade? Sometimes he wondered.

Suddenly the phone rang and Gail shouted from the kitchen, "Scott, it's for you!"

Scott lunged across the hallway and picked up the phone in his bedroom. A woman's voice came across the line. "Scott? This is Wendy's mom. Listen, Wendy just got home from the hairdresser and her hair is . . . well, it's a disaster."

"Oh no, I'm sure it looks fine," Scott tried to console.

"It should after we're done taking it all down and starting from scratch. Could you come about fifteen minutes later?"

Scott agreed. He hung up the phone and plopped down at his desk.

Now what?

He grabbed the green notebook—his journal—from the top drawer and flipped halfway through, stopping at a blank page. He began to write:

I've been looking forward to this prom for weeks and it's finally here.

His eyes shot to the digital clock on his nightstand and he suddenly slammed the notebook shut. *I can't write in my journal now—I'm too nervous.* So he headed back to the bathroom to brush his teeth for the fifth time and splash on another palmful of Dad's cologne. Later, when he walked into the living room, his parents looked up from the evening news to croon over their eighteen-year-old son.

"Scott! You look so handsome!" Gail smiled up at him.

"Fine looking tux, son," Chuck added. "Very nice."

"Well, I think I'm all set," Scott said, his voice suddenly high-pitched and laced with anxiety. "You sure I look okay?"

"Better than okay," Chuck returned. "Great. Just great." Gail went to the kitchen to get the corsage. As she handed it to Scott, she reached up and kissed him on the cheek.

"Wendy's a lucky girl to be going to the prom with a catch like you," she said, straightening his already-straight bow tie. She tugged at his cummerbund and stood back to size him up. Her beaming smile said it all.

Scott squared his shoulders, swiped his keys off the coffee table, and turned toward the door. "Don't wait up."

About a block from Wendy's house, Scott stopped his blue Maverick at a red light and snuck a quick look at himself in the rear-view mirror. He wiped a glaze of perspiration from his forehead and reached to turn up the air conditioning. His car crawled along in front of a row of brown and white houses. *They all look the same,* he thought. *Which one is it?* He grabbed the scrawled map off the dashboard and checked the address. He braked suddenly and put the car in reverse, backtracking four houses. Before the engine was shut off, a bevy of children had gathered in the front yard to ogle at him.

"Are you Wendy's date?" asked a little girl in dirty pink overalls.

"You should've seen her hair an hour ago," another girl said. "You better be glad my mom fixed it."

"Is this like a prom or something?" asked a boy in a Dodger jersey. Scott smiled and nodded and hurried toward the door—it opened before he could ring the bell. Before him stood a brown-haired man with glasses perched on top of his head. His blue-striped tie was loosened, and a newspaper hung from one hand. His expression was stolid, bland.

"Hope the kids aren't bothering you," he said in monotone.

"No, no problem."

"I'm Wendy's father. You must be Scott. C'mon in."

Scott wiped sweaty palms on his pantlegs and walked into

the sunny living room. The father plunked down in a La-Z-Boy recliner and tossed his newspaper aside. Scott sank deep into the green and white brocade couch opposite him. He gripped the corsage box in both hands and emitted an audible sigh.

"So, Wendy tells me you plan on going to Western Christian College next year."

Oh great, Scott thought, *here it comes. Twenty questions.*

"Yeah, I do . . . I am. That's my plan anyway. I'm saving my money."

"And what do you plan on studying?"

"Uh, I'm not really sure at this point," Scott stammered. "I like photography and writing . . . or maybe music." *Music? What a stupid thing to say. I have no intention of studying music!*

"So are you going to be working this summer then?"

"Yeah. I heard about a job at a pie shop. Waiter, you know. It's . . . it's really a better job than it sounds. Good tips, anyway," Scott finished weakly.

The interrogation was cut short as Wendy's mom entered the room beaming. "Scott? We spoke on the phone. How nice to meet you." She exuded a maternal glow. "Wendy'll be out in a minute." Scott unbuttoned his tux jacket and felt a bead of sweat trickle from his armpit. An awkward silence ensued.

"I can't believe graduation is next week," Scott said, trying to ease the tension. "Will you be able to make it?"

"Sure. How many times does a dad get to see his daughter graduate from high school?" Wendy's dad said dryly.

"Wouldn't miss it for the world," Wendy's mom chimed in sincerely from across the room where she was picking up toys. Another few seconds of deafening silence lingered before being shattered by two little girls bursting through the front door.

"Mom, when's dinner?" the older one asked.

"In a little while, dear. Did you meet Scott?"

The younger, pigtailed girl turned to glower at Scott, her eyes squinting, her arms crossed. "Are you going to marry my sister?" she asked without hesitation. Scott's face immediately swelled to a cherry-tomato red.

"I'd like to get through the prom first," he answered.

"Becky, you're not supposed to ask questions like that," her mom scolded. "Leave him alone."

Wendy strolled out from the hall not a minute too soon. "Hi, Scott. I'm ready to go," she sing-songed. Scott stared at her wide-eyed, mouth slightly agape. She looked stunning, wearing a spaghetti-strapped gown of blue chiffon that matched her eyes. Her ash-blonde hair was piled neatly atop her head, her neck and shoulders milk-white and inviting. Scott held out the corsage box to her and managed a smile.

"Oh, how sweet. It's beautiful," she gushed. "Would you like to pin it on?"

Scott grasped the three-inch pin in one tremulous hand and the whorl of roses and baby's-breath in the other. He rebuked himself for not getting the wrist corsage, while panicking over the prospect of finding the appropriate placement between Wendy's neckline and her, um. . . . An eternity of seconds passed while he stared painfully at the corsage, forced two coughs to stall, and took a tentative step toward his date.

"Oh, those things can be so tricky," Wendy's mom said, bolting from her chair across the room. "Why don't you let me do that? We wouldn't want to get any blood on this new dress." She cackled and unloaded Scott's hands.

The pinned, preened, and polished couple escaped the house amid a flurry of farewells and happy wishes:

"Goodbye!"

"Have a wonderful time."

"You look lovely."

"Don't be too late!"

"Goodnight, Princess."

The prom itself was special only because it was theirs. Otherwise, it was typical of a thousand other high school proms: guys looking stiff in rented tuxes; girls hanging proudly on their dates' arms; photos snapped in front of an airbrushed backdrop; starry-eyed gazes beneath shimmering lights; guys stepping on girls' toes on the dance floor and girls pretending not to mind; the austere librarian guarding the punch bowl against would-be spikers; red punch tasting strangely like the kind at church socials; more toes on toes; and finally the last romantic dance below soft lights and sagging streamers.

Heading home, Scott's blue Maverick crept along beneath the hazy yellow glow of street lamps. The street was quiet and deserted. It was 2:30 in the morning, but neither Scott nor Wendy was tired. They had spent the past two hours driving around the city, walking on the beach, and drinking coffee at an all-night café. They had talked the entire time – about school, graduation, memories, and future plans. Now Scott turned off the headlights three houses away and braked the car to a stop in front of Wendy's house. He hopped out of the car and opened Wendy's door. He took her hand to help her out. They walked silently up the driveway toward the front door. There was only a dim kitchen light on – the rest of the house was dark.

"Well, Scott, thanks again for a great time," Wendy said almost from nowhere, her face masked in darkness.

"It was my pleasure – thank you for being my date," he said.

"It was so much fun. You're . . . you're sweet."

Scott took an imperceptible step toward her on the shadowy porch. The seconds ticked by in silence. A dog barked in the distance. Wendy's face was obscured and undefined in the porch's cool gray shadows, but Scott remembered every detail. His hands reached out to her – their hands found each other in the darkness and tightened around one another. Scott stepped closer.

Suddenly, like lightning, a white light flooded the porch. The front door swung open and out popped Wendy's father's head.

"Did you have a good time?" he asked in a booming voice. His glasses still rested atop his wavy brown hair, and the shoulder of his maroon bathrobe muscled through the open door.

"Uh, yes, Daddy, we sure did," Wendy answered.

"Sure did, sir," Scott said sullenly, taking a quick baby-step backward.

"Well, thanks again, Scott," Wendy almost interrupted him. "I guess I'll see you on Monday. Uh, thanks."

"Okay, see you then. Goodnight. Goodnight, sir."

The door closed, and Scott lumbered away. He stopped and stood in the driveway staring up at Wendy's window. A minute passed and a light illuminated the curtain. He waited, but her silhouette didn't darken the yellow-hued window. He got in the car and drove away slowly. A smile began to play on his face. As he passed street lights and occasional cars, thoughts flooded Scott's mind, thoughts that would later find their way into his journal: *Maybe I've finally found someone I can love. Perhaps all these years of heartbreaking loneliness will soon be over. I've ached for a special, intimate friend for so long. People are just so shallow . . . but not Wendy. I can be myself with her. And she seems to like me—just for who I am. It was such a wonderful night—what a night! I'm so glad Wendy had a good time. It was great to go with the girl I really like. Oh, thank You, Lord, for giving me such a wonderful time.*

A car pulled up next to Scott's at a red light with its radio blasting. Scott rolled up the window to regain his solitude and his thoughts. The light turned green, and the car screeched away. *It seems like I'm always the one who reaches out—and gets rejected. For years it's been that way. Church friends, school friends. Like Paul Reardon—I've really tried to get close to him, but he's so superficial. He rejected my friendship. I just wanted someone to share my life with, someone who would be my special, close friend. I feel I have so much to give; I feel things so deeply.*

It was 3:15 by the time Scott finally slipped his key in the lock and quietly sidled through the doorway. He flipped on the light in his room and tossed his tuxedo jacket over the back of his chair. The bowtie had long since been removed and now he reached around to unbuckle his cummerbund.

Kicking off his shoes, he fell backwards onto his bed and stared up at the ceiling. Behind him rose a wall full of comic books neatly arranged in three oak bookcases—the legacy of a childhood hobby; a world of fantasy that had filled his mind with faraway places, creatures with superhuman abilities, and wild, exciting adventures.

Scott stared up at the frosted-glass light fixture on the ceiling—a veritable cemetery for moths and other bugs. His stuffed animals still sat loyally on his dresser top. The Bible rested open to the Twenty-third Psalm. The room was a museum of childhood memories, and yet a vista of the future. College catalogs and applications sat companionably next to elementary school scrapbooks and Hardy Boys' mystery books.

He propped himself up and dangled a foot off the edge of the bed, then spotted the green notebook where he had left it earlier that evening. He eyed it for a moment, deciding whether or not he was too tired to write in the journal. But the excitement of the evening smothered all hint of fatigue. He grabbed the notebook and a pen from the desk. He quickly filled two pages with details of the night and finished the entry with the line that had danced in his mind all evening:

Maybe I've finally found someone I can love.

Imagine being this close to love, when for so many years it had felt so very far away!

Scott sat quietly for several minutes, absorbed in his own thoughts. Then, slowly, he turned to the front of the journal, to some of the earliest entries, and began to thumb through the pages.

It was hard not to notice certain words that peppered the pages in his hands. They appeared so often, they seemed to leap off the paper and into Scott's line of sight as he skimmed the entries: *loneliness . . . love . . . pain . . . friendship . . . hurt.*

And one other word: *Paul.*

Paul Reardon was a theme that ran through Scott's journal like a river through a parched and thirsty land. Sometimes the water flowed and there was hope. Many times the gully ran bone-dry, the hope long gone, leaving only the scar.

From five years ago, Scott read:

I'm so lonely. This loneliness eats at my inner soul! I long for close friends so badly! There's one friend that I'd especially like to know better. His name is Paul Reardon, and if he loved me as much as I care for him, I'd be the happiest person alive!

From three years ago:

Best friends are beautiful to watch together because they love each other so deeply! I've longed for a best friend for such a long time, but the Lord hasn't granted me one yet. I often think of Paul. I guess he's been too busy to think much of me. We're in a couple of classes together, and sometimes we talk about school and stuff. But it's not enough. I want more. I want to be best friends.

And from just last Christmas:

I know for my own peace of mind that I should stop thinking of Paul, but I can't. He hurts me so deeply; he continually overlooks my attempts at a close, intimate friendship. Why? Why can't he love me the way I love him? If there's a spark of love in Paul's heart for me, then I'll somehow get it to flame.

Scott began to feel the familiar ache of loneliness. After five years of knowing the towheaded surfer, they were hardly more than casual friends. It was a far, far cry from the close camaraderie that Scott longed for.

Scott closed his journal. These were secret longings, shared only with God and within the pages of the green notebook. They were secret hurts, that no one would ever begin to suspect. Sometimes Scott wished he could talk about the loneliness that seemed to gnaw at his very soul.

But who would listen? Who would understand?

Then he remembered Wendy, and he smiled just a little.

Perhaps, if he had someone like Wendy at his side, being best friends with Paul Reardon wouldn't matter quite so much. . . .

The last week of high school sped by, brimming with the kinds of events and goodbyes that leave seniors too busy to relish the moment, but become the stuff of fond memories later. On the very last day of school, Scott sat on a bench in Senior Square.

With mere hours till graduation, the campus was nearly empty, though a few classmates still milled around. Occasionally someone passed Scott with a brief greeting or wave. Several friends stopped by with their yearbooks and asked Scott to sign.

Scott sat alone, writing in a yearbook when a freckled girl approached him. She stood patiently, waiting for him to look up. He continued writing. She finally took a step to her right, casting a shadow on the page Scott was signing. He started.

"Melanie! Oh, hi! I didn't see you there."

"What are you writing? The great American novel?" she said playfully.

"Nah. Although I guess it *is* a little long." He shrugged down at the page, already three-quarters filled with his writing.

"Who's it to? *Wendy?*" There was an edge to Melanie's voice. Scott looked up, surprised.

"Uh, no. It's to a friend. Paul . . . Paul Reardon."

"Oh. Well, thanks for your note . . . about the older guy from church. As usual, your advice about my love life is right on. And . . . it sort of fits in with what I've been feeling the last couple days."

"Oh?"

"Yeah. I guess there is plenty of time for *older* men. I've got a lot of good friends . . . and good dating prospects . . . right around here."

"Around here." Scott said the words slowly, gazing at the now-empty campus. "Not for long, kiddo. It's all over but the shoutin'."

"What's that supposed to mean?" Melanie smoothed her pants and sat down on the bench next to Scott.

"Nothing." Scott shrugged. "I guess I'm just sitting here being nostalgic. I'm really gonna miss this place. The yearbook staff, drama, student council. . . ."

"Scott, I'd totally forgotten all the things you were involved with."

"Yeah, about the only thing I missed was sports. Sports were just never my thing, I guess." He paused and looked at the ground. "That and friendship."

"What! That's stupid! You've got lots of friends." Melanie rebuked him with a punch in the arm. "You're one of the most popular guys on campus."

"I don't know."

"Are you sure it's not end-of-the-year blues? You know, saying goodbye to friends, teachers, and all that? I mean, you always seem so happy. . . ."

"It's hard to explain." Scott chipped away peeling green paint from the weathered bench. "I feel like I'm missing something . . . or someone. Sometimes I just feel . . . lonely." Scott bit his lip. He could hardly tell Melanie his heart still smarted from yesterday, when he saw Wendy Dolen flirting with one of the guys from the swim team. *The big love of my life,* he thought sarcastically, *and I'll probably never get the guts to ask for a second date.*

Melanie stared at Scott, shielding her eyes from the late afternoon sun. "Look. Tonight's graduation. Tomorrow you're done with high school and it's a brand new start. When you get to college, you're going to meet a ton of new people . . . all new friends. Don't give up now. This is just the beginning for you."

Melanie looked at her watch then jumped to her feet. "Darn! I'm meeting some friends at the mall and I'm late." She scooped up her books from the bench, sliding one out from the rest and handing it to Scott. "And I almost forgot this, too. I promised I'd get it back before graduation, and here it is. See you tonight?"

"Of course." Scott watched Melanie hurry off, then cracked open his yearbook and skimmed the pages for her message. He found it in the ad section, beneath a graduation greeting from the local mortuary. He read:

Scott,
    You're such a trip, but you make my life interesting. Thanks again for your friendship, all your helpful advice, and for keeping me awake in Western Civ. Good luck in the future. I hope you find the pot of gold at the end of your rainbow . . . and may she be beautiful.

THREE

Laughing on the Outside

T he brunette in the navy sweater exploded with laughter, drawing stares from the other college students eating in the university cafeteria. Between rounds, she managed to gasp, "You're . . . you're making this up. Scott Cameron, if you're lying. . . ."

Scott smiled broadly beneath a deep summer tan. "No, I swear, Colleen. It's true."

"And then what happened?" a second girl prompted.

"Well," Scott paused. Looking down at his lunch tray, he loaded up another forkful of "spaghetti surprise." He put it in his mouth, chewing slowly.

Colleen punched him in the arm. "No stalling!"

Scott swallowed loudly. "Okay, okay. So, I finally straightened out the wrong dorm assignment. I was humiliated in the cafeteria line when the cashier didn't have my name for a meal ticket. They assigned me a campus mailbox somewhere in Washington State with the Z's because someone forgot to include my name, Cameron, in with the C's. And then. . . ."

"And then?"

"And then, today, they posted the names of all the freshmen, along with our student I.D. numbers. Well, I spent ten minutes trying to find my name. And I wasn't on the list. So I trekked back to admissions—for about the fiftieth time in the three days

I've been here on campus—and asked to talk with someone new, someone who hopefully could help me solve this thing once and for all."

"And did they?" Colleen asked over her glass of diet soda.

"Well . . ." Scott hedged.

"Did you see Mrs. Brennan? She helped me before." The second girl, Jody, spoke through a full mouth.

"That was the one." Scott nodded. "Mrs. Brennan. She was really nice. She pulled my file and looked over everything . . . my transcripts, references, application . . . and then she said, 'Well, everything seems to be in order. I know you feel you've been overlooked around here, but I'm sure it was just a temporary condition. I'm sure it won't happen again, Steve.'"

"Steve?" Jody howled. "She called you *Steve?*"

Colleen was too busy laughing to comment. Finally, she said, "You must be having a real identity crisis, Scott. Maybe you showed up at the wrong college. Ever think of that?"

Colleen, Jody, and Scott burst into fresh volleys of laughter.

Suddenly Scott choked as someone slapped him from behind. He caught his breath. The girls were laughing again. He turned around to face his assailant. It was Will, Scott's new roommate.

Will grinned and shook his head. "What's going on over here, a party? How do you expect people to concentrate enough to figure out what they're eating in here? Ladies," he addressed the girls, "I hope my roommate is behaving himself."

The girls giggled.

Will winked at Scott before rejoining friends at another table. "Go for it, buddy," he said in a low voice. But not low enough. The girls giggled again.

Scott flushed a red to match his hair. But through the burn, his eyes met Colleen's. *Maybe,* he thought to himself, *just maybe I will.*

After lunch, Scott escaped the California September heat by retreating to his dorm room. He straightened his desk, hung a few posters, and arranged his new textbooks, three of which were for his journalism classes.

Scott hoped to be a writer someday. He joked about writing

the great American novel. Sometimes he even toyed with the titles he would give a book about his life.

But all that was for the future. Right now, the only stories about his life were to be found in his volumes of journals. Scott unpacked a final box from home and pulled out a brand new notebook and an unopened package of school paper. He knew Will was playing Ping-Pong in the student center, so it seemed a good time to break in his newest journal with updates of orientation week. Sitting at his desk, the words tumbled over each other and onto the page:

I'm only forty-five minutes from home — but it feels much farther than that. Almost like another world. College. It feels so . . . so grown up. I'm really glad I picked a Christian school. There's a feeling about this place. Like it's. . . .

He paused to think.

. . . like it's right. I mean, I really feel like this is exactly where God wants me to be right now. I've been so lonely. Really lonely. But this is like a whole new start. Melanie was right. There's so many new friends here. Like my roommate, Will. And Jody, this girl from Wisconsin. And Colleen. Colleen is, well, she's beautiful.

Scott stopped, chewed the end of his pencil for a moment, then began to write again.

We took the most awful test this week — all incoming students had to take it. It was a personality test called the M.M.P.I., and it was weird! I had to agree or disagree with statements like, "I have diarrhea at least once a month," "My mother was a good woman," "I see imaginary animals and people that no one else sees," and "Someone is trying to poison me." It was hard not to laugh — in fact, there were some other kids sitting behind me and we joked about parts of the test all the way through. I could see which questions were written to discover symptoms of weird

*mental things. Like schizophrenia. And being paranoid. And
homosexuality, too. I could tell. That was one of the things they
were looking for.*

Scott started to close his journal, thought again, and scribbled a quick P.S.:

*But other than that weird test—and the fact that it took three
days to get my name on their computer system around here—
college is great. Really great. I can already tell . . . things are
going to be different for me. This is just the start of a whole new
beginning.*

Scott laid the journal on one of the shelves above his desk.
On the same shelf, a stack of envelopes waited to be mailed. As
the summer had drawn to a close and Scott began packing for
college, he had promised high school friends that he'd write once
a week. Now, he picked up the stack of letters, written last night
to a half-dozen friends. The campus post office would close in
fifteen minutes, and he still needed to buy stamps. He would have
to hurry.

He made the trek across campus with three minutes to
spare. He fumbled in his pocket for the correct change, then slid
the letters across the post office counter. The cashier stamped
the envelopes with a meter, then dropped them in a gray mailbag.
The name on the very top letter was visible for an instant before
the stack dropped out of sight.

That letter was addressed to Paul Reardon.

In the following weeks, Scott's idealism regarding college life collided with reality.

A third of the way into the semester, Scott had yet to hear
back from many of the high school friends he had been writing faithfully, including Wendy Dolen, another classmate named
Kirk Graham, and, of course, Paul. To make matters worse, Scott
found himself immersed in his first exams. And life with a room-

mate wasn't quite as glamorous as Scott had always thought. As much as Scott liked Will, there was something inherently annoying about someone who sat in the middle of the room and clipped his toenails onto the carpet. There was also the problem of radically different tastes in music and study habits. And then there had been the discovery that Colleen, the girl in the navy sweater, had a boyfriend back home, and another discovery that one of Scott's research papers had fallen into his dirty laundry bag and disintegrated in the wash.

Any way he looked at it, this wasn't quite the wonderful new beginning that Scott had hoped for five weeks ago. Any way he looked at it, the stress was beginning to build.

It was a quarter to midnight when Scott closed his textbook and decided to call it quits for the night. Will was already in bed on his side of the room, but he wasn't asleep yet. As Scott returned from the bathroom, toothbrush in hand, Will looked up from something he was reading and shook his head.

"Can you believe this?" Will waved a piece of paper at Scott, who was now digging in the closet for his favorite sweats.

"What it is?" Scott's voice was muffled, coming from the bottom of the closet.

"It's depressing, that's what it is."

Scott stood, sweats in hand. He climbed into the pants, tightened the drawstring, and pulled a faded sweat shirt down over his head before answering. "Lemme see." He crossed the room and took the paper from Will's hand. "A letter?"

"Yeah. From a friend back home. But man, is she in the dumps." Will lounged easily against the pillows, his lap strewn with several opened envelopes and additional letters. Will always seemed to get mail.

"In the dumps? Why?"

"Lonely. She's really lonely. And here's another." He extracted a second paper from the pile and handed it to Scott. "His name's Tim. Too bad I can't introduce the two of them to each other. Tim's really lonely, too."

"Why can't you introduce them?"

Will shrugged. "Tim moved away with his folks. He's somewhere in Arkansas. Patty—the girl—is still in Wisconsin. But that's not the point. It's great to have friends and everything, but some people go too far. I mean, they get to the point where that's all they think about. They worship the idea of friendship. Sometimes I think that's where Tim is . . . and Patty too."

"Maybe if they had some, they wouldn't have to be so consumed by it," Scott said, a little too quickly.

"Oh, I don't know. If you're obsessed with something, that doesn't mean getting it will solve all your problems. Besides, who said Tim and Patty don't have friends?"

"Yeah?"

Will shrugged. "Sure. They're both pretty popular. At least they were when I was home . . . and before Tim moved. No, I think if someone's obsessed with something, there's a deeper problem that caused them to go off the deep end in the beginning. Y'know what I mean?"

"I . . . I guess so. I don't know."

Will continued. "Patty and Tim are so lonely for friends, they rank friendship above everything else. Above school. Family. Even their relationship with God. If they got more friends, what would that solve? They'd still neglect school, family, God . . . maybe even more so. They're off-balance now. I don't think they need more friends."

"No?"

"No. I think they need to figure out what's going on inside. They need to figure out why the heck they're so lonely they can't see straight."

Scott handed back the letters with some comment about needing to get up early for class. He crossed the room and crawled into bed with a brief "G'night."

Will stared. "Hey, man, what about the lights? At least turn off the lights."

Scott rolled over, grabbed a sneaker from under his bed, and flung it at the light switch across the room. He missed and knocked a plaque off the wall. He groped for the second shoe. It sailed after the first. The room went black.

Shaking his head, Will dropped the letters onto the floor.

Less than five minutes after hitting the pillow, he fell fast asleep. Two hours later, Scott was still awake, staring into the dark.

Several days later, Scott wrote about their midnight conversation in his journal. He closed with these words:

Maybe I've been overdoing it with all the letters to my friends—letters that no one seems to answer. Maybe I'm trying too hard. Maybe it's true: I'm obsessed.

Why do I knock myself out like this?

I guess it's because I don't feel I belong to anyone. I mean, it seems as though I'm always forcing my friendship on people. I'm never sought out anymore, and people get along fine without me. I want to be needed! I want to be missed! I thought it might be different here, at school, surrounded by people my age. The setting's different, but the loneliness is the same.

Oh, I can't complain like this. The Lord has blessed me in so many ways and has answered so many of my prayers in the past. I'll just have to be patient and wait a little longer for His answers on this one. But Lord, please answer soon.

I'm hurting on the inside.

"Tammy! Over here!" Scott stretched and waved to a cluster of girls across the crowded game room. One of the girls broke away from the group and started toward him. The other girls followed, weaving past Ping-Pong tables, dodging balls, and slowing once to sneak stares at a tanned Tom Cruise look-alike pounding out a round of space aliens on a video arcade machine.

Tammy stretched to give her brother a quick hug. She was small and fiery, just like Gail, and one year younger than the brother she alternately plagued and adored. Scott returned the hug, then greeted the other three girls, all friends from church.

Tammy bubbled, "Scott, this was such a good idea. Why didn't we think of this sooner? Lunch at a real college cafeteria!"

Scott laughed. "Reserve judgment until you've tasted the food. This way, ladies." He led the way out of the student center and down a flight of cement steps.

"Where's the cafeteria?" one of the girls asked Scott.

"You can't miss it, Janine. Just look for the ambulances."

"Scott! I'm sure!" Janine squealed.

"I know where it is," one of the other girls announced. "It's next to the science center. In a round building, with lots of windows."

"Is she right, Scott?" Tammy wanted to know.

"Yep. You must have been here before," Scott addressed the girl who seemed to know the way. She was grinning wildly, ready to burst with some news.

"I was here last month, on a *date* with a sophomore!"

The other girls squealed.

"Actually it was a double date—Wendy Dolen was here too. Our dates were roommates. We saw a movie, then came on campus for an ice-cream bash in the cafeteria."

Scott stopped walking. "You were on a double date with Wendy?"

"Yeah. Oh, I almost forgot. I saw her yesterday and told her we were meeting you for lunch today. She said to say 'hi.'"

"'Hi'? Just 'hi'?" Scott caught the serious tone in his voice, then forced a grin. "After all we meant to each other?" He clutched his heart dramatically.

"That's right!" Janine pointed at Scott, remembering. "Didn't you guys go to the senior prom last year or something?"

Last year . . . last year. She makes it sound so ancient, instead of four short months ago.

"Yeah. It was no big deal, though. We were just friends," Scott lied through his teeth.

"Let's not talk about *that*," Tammy glared. "I told Scott he should have gone with someone else. Wendy's so popular, she could have gotten a hundred dates. And there were a lot of girls at school who didn't have anyone to take them."

"Tammy, don't start this again," Scott warned.

"Scott, you know it's true," Tammy whined. "You just liked Wendy as a friend. You told me so. You might as well have gone with one of our other friends who didn't get asked. Like Melanie. I'll bet Wendy got at least ten invites."

"I know somebody who wanted to go with Scott," Janine offered in a sing-song voice.

"So do I," Tammy added. "I know a lot of girls."

"Enough, guys. This is embarrassing. Anyway, we're here." Scott stopped in front of a domed building with panoramic windows and held the door open for his guests.

". . . just that he's really popular, and lots of girls wanted to go with him," Tammy was telling the others as they entered the building. "It would have been different if he'd really *liked* Wendy."

"Maybe he really did," Janine offered. "Maybe he just didn't tell you."

"No, I could tell. I know my brother, and I could tell."

Scott changed the subject with some question about church. But his heart wasn't in the new conversation, and he quickly fell silent. He watched Tammy for a moment, chattering happily with her friends.

You'd be surprised how much you don't know, little sister. You'd be very surprised.

The weeks slipped toward Valentine's Day, and on February 14, Scott found himself without any real romantic interest in his life. Wendy was still dating the sophomore from Scott's college, and Colleen—the girl in the navy sweater—was still hooked on the guy back home. Sitting alone in the campus coffee shop, amid happy couples and cliques of friends, Scott nursed a cup of hot chocolate and filled his journal with thoughts about love:

We had the most meaningful all-campus chapel this morning! The speaker said that the true test of love is whether or not you're willing to give; and the true measure of love is how much you'll give.

Another man closed with a song, and the lyrics went something like: "When you stop burning with love, someone will die from the cold."

Oh, but that hits home!

Many times lately I've thought, "Why do I continue to love—and write to—friends like Wendy, Kirk, and others? Especially Paul. None of these friends seems to love me as much as I love them. Sometimes I think I'm obsessed, that I'm wasting my time, that I'll never find the kind of intimate friendship I'm looking for. And that I'll never shake this deep, deep loneliness.

But that song I heard today. . . I never considered that when I stop burning with love for others, someone may die from the cold.

There was something else the chapel speaker said, on this Valentine's Day. He said there was a time all his friends were getting married, and he hadn't even met anyone special yet. He said that it really hurt, but he finally came to the point where he could say, "God, I give the whole situation over to You. If You think it's best for me to marry, I know You'll allow me to meet my bride in Your perfect timing. And if You think it's best for me to remain single, then it's You and me all the way. I'll be satisfied."

He went on to say that a week later he met the girl he later married, and that she had come to know Jesus Christ personally on the very day he said that prayer.

I, too, prayed that prayer this evening.

It seems as though I'll never marry—for a variety of reasons. And it hurts so much! But I trust the Lord. I guess my relationship with Him had better be strong; I have a feeling it will have to see me through an awful lot in the coming years.

The following months, brimming with all the challenge, fun, and frustrations of college life, began to settle into somewhat of a pattern. Chapel in the mornings, gym twice a week, lunchtime with friends, and classes till 11:30 or 3:00, depending on the day of the week. Most evenings meant dorm activities, a burger with the guys, an occasional movie with a girl, or studying in the library.

Afternoons, however, took on a life of their own, far, far removed from campus routines. That's when Scott settled into the dorm lounge and flipped on the television, searching the channels until he found *Ryan's Hope,* the daily soap that had captured his imagination. Some evenings, Scott loaded up his Maverick with friends and took off for downtown Hollywood to the Harlequin, an ornate theater specializing in his most recent passion: classic movies from the '20s, '30s, and '40s. While the daily soaps seemed to glamorize the disillusionment rampant in his own life, the big screen classics offered something Scott was beginning to wonder if he would ever experience firsthand: romance, true love, and a happy ending.

On weekends Scott drove back home, chatted with his folks, exchanged verbal rounds with Tammy, and played with the family's cocker spaniel, Sparkle. He also attended church, taught a junior high Bible class, and sang in the choir. He sang in the tenor section—along with Paul Reardon, who had just recently joined.

Paul again.

Sunday mornings were bearable, when preoccupation with the service and their performance kept conversations between choir members brief and to the point. But Sunday afternoon choir rehearsals were harder. Then, the easy banter between the vocalists left Scott aching for more. Any comment, casual and meaningless, from Paul could spark a flame that wasn't easy to douse.

After one such Sunday in April, Scott wrote in his journal:

I still feel uncomfortable around Paul. For so long I've wanted so much to be very best friends with him . . . it's hard to be with him, casually, in choir. Things take time, though, and I'm not asking God to change Paul—I'm asking him to change me.

I want to be free of these obsessions with friendships. And I want to be free from the loneliness. But most of all, I want to be a whole person . . . totally me . . . not bits and pieces. Not divided by all the awful things I feel inside. Not two people—one who laughs and jokes and smiles on the outside, while the other Scott cries on the inside.

I guess the worst part of it all is that I feel I'm living a very wasted life. I know what I'd really like to do with my life, but it's so wrong. I know I have friends who love me and who would stick by me in the midst of the worst times . . . and I consider this to be one of the very worst times, even though it's just not evident from my outward appearance.

There it is again. Laughing on the outside, crying on the inside.

I just want to be whole. That's all. I just want to be whole.

One Sunday morning, as the sanctuary emptied toward the parking lot, Tony Lozano caught up with Scott on his way to his Maverick. After graduating from high school with Scott, Tony had landed a job loading boxes at the local United Parcel office. For the past ten months, he had been working hard and saving money to tie the knot with his high-school sweetheart, Caroline.

But that morning, it wasn't his own relationship that had him concerned.

"Hey, Scotty. Heard the rumors?" Tony asked as he and Scott approached the car.

Scott shook his head, fumbling in his pocket for his car keys.

"It's scary, man. Stuff about Bob Sloan resigning. There's stuff about a *divorce.*"

Scott stopped walking, stopped reaching for his keys, and simply stared at Tony. "No way! That's impossible. I saw him and Margie together this morning. They seem fine."

Tony shook his head. "Uh-uh. There's a custody battle for the children and everything. I heard he'll take an extended leave of absence from his job at the church. They're getting someone else to fill in as choir director."

Scott's heart sunk at the news.

That afternoon, at choir rehearsal, there was no official announcement about Bob's absence. But Bob wasn't there, and someone named Steve had suddenly taken his place.

One week later, an associate pastor showed up at choir rehearsal with the news: "Bob and his wife are filing for divorce, and the church thinks it would be better if he didn't work while going through this crisis in his personal life. Bob's not fired . . . in fact, he's still on the payroll. But maybe it's best if he didn't have a leadership position in the church while he's trying to work things out at home."

Scott didn't hear anything new about Bob for two or three weeks. Then one Sunday afternoon, just after Steve, the new director, headed out the sanctuary door, there was a noise at the rear of the sanctuary. The back door swung wide and in strode Bob.

Bob was immediately surrounded. The greetings and questions flew fast. Bob gave generalizations about the divorce, said that he was doing okay, and explained that he just wanted to see the old gang, but didn't feel comfortable running into any of the pastoral staff.

So he hid. And waited. And took the opportunity to sneak in when the coast was clear.

Only Scott, Paul Reardon, and a few others stood back, away from the clamoring crowd in the center of the sanctuary.

A few minutes later, Scott and Paul slipped out unnoticed and headed together toward their cars in the parking lot. They were silent for several yards, and then Scott shook his head. "I love Bob and all, and I want him with us at rehearsals, but not like that."

"I know what you mean," Paul nodded.

"Not *sneaking*."

"I agree. But what could we do?" Paul asked. "We couldn't ask him to leave."

"Maybe not, but he shouldn't have come."

"Maybe the church is being too hard on him, Scott."

"I . . . I don't know. I really don't. But something's not right, I'll tell you that."

"I don't know what *you* think it is," Paul said, "but I'll tell you what bugs *me*."

"What?"

Paul shrugged. "Supposedly Bob's marriage has been hurting for a while, right?"

"Right."

"That means Bob's been going through a lot. A lot of pain, I'd guess."

"Yeah, I'd guess," Scott agreed.

"So how come nobody knew?"

"What do you mean?"

"We were just about as close to him as anybody," Paul explained. "By 'we' I mean the choir. He was the director, but he was like one of 'us.' Always joking with us, talking with us, praying with us."

"Yeah?"

"And nobody knew." Paul stopped walking and turned to face his friend. "Bob was hurting all along, and nobody knew. He never told a soul. And then all of a sudden, the whole thing blows sky high."

"Maybe . . . maybe he thought nobody would understand," Scott said slowly.

"Yeah, maybe." Paul shrugged. "But he never gave us a chance. And now he'll never really know for sure, will he?"

FOUR

The Eagle Flies Alone

The weeks warmed toward summer. On the first Sunday morning of Scott's summer vacation, Scott walked into his college group classroom at church and was met by a too-perky co-ed who shoved a flyer into his hand. She bubbled, "Hi, Scott, don't forget about next month's retreat. It's going to be great!" He barely had a chance to nod before she flitted to the next newcomer.

Scott headed toward the back of the room, past walls plastered with posters advertising upcoming barbecues, pool parties, and retreats. Just past a knot of chattering women in bright-colored dresses, he picked out a seat and settled in. His eyes skimmed the flyer in his hands.

"Hey, there you are, Scott. I was looking for you." Kirk Graham, tan with sandy-blond hair, accented his greeting by giving Scott a quick slap on the back.

"Hi, Kirk." Scott looked up to return the smile.

"Just wanted to say I got your letter this week. Man, you're such a good letter writer. I wish I were better." Kirk winced. "But I don't have to tell you that—you already know that's not one of my strengths."

Scott shrugged, then stood to look Kirk in the eye. He smiled. "No sweat. I seem to have everybody beat at that skill, but I'm getting used to it."

"I'm gonna write back this time. Promise."

"Great. You'll have three months to do it in, too, 'cause I'm home now for summer vaca . . . ."

"Hey, you guys," a short, curly-topped guy from the next row of chairs leaned into the conversation. He lowered his voice to mask the glee it held. "You hear about Jenny Wilcox and Kim Myers?"

"No," Kirk answered. "I don't think. . . ."

"They're *lesbians*," the intruder blurted.

"Give me a break, Marty. Where'd you hear that?" Scott said curtly.

"Melanie told me. It's true! Melanie's friends with both of them," Marty defended. "I guess it started in high school. I always thought those two were a little strange."

"I don't think you ought to be saying stuff like that, man," Kirk chimed in. "You don't know. . . . Not for sure." Kirk turned on his heel and walked away while Marty continued filling Scott's ear in hushed tones. The college pastor, stood behind the podium and tried to quiet the din of yammering people.

"Okay, everyone grab a seat," he said. "We're going to start in just a second."

As Marty scurried off to friends across the room, Scott dropped into his seat and dug his hands deep into the pockets of his blue corduroys. He half-listened to the announcements and managed to mouth a few of the songs. He shifted his weight and crossed his legs as the pastor began to talk: "Today, I want to talk about self-esteem—how you view yourself. Your self-image is one of the most crucial elements in your relationships with friends, your relationship with God, as well as your happiness and fulfillment in life. . . ."

Twenty minutes later, the pastor handed out a one-page questionnaire to help everyone examine his or her self-image. Scott scribbled a few answers, but his thoughts kept pulling him back to Marty's accusation about the two high school friends. Why were people so fascinated with the failings of others? Marty had been quick to judge and quick to gossip . . . and quick to take a perverse pleasure in the whole process.

But Scott also had to wonder: If the story were true, why

hadn't the girls looked for help before their struggles hit the rumor mill? Scott's thoughts drifted to Bob and Margie Sloan, their divorce now public and the battle over their children turning pretty hostile.

They'd had their secrets, too.

Scott shook the thoughts from his mind, then skimmed the page in his hand until he came to the last question: "Do you like yourself? Why or why not?" He stared at the corner of the sheet with squinted eyes and wrinkled brow, thinking, then sat upright and began to write his answer. For a single, isolated moment, his pen opened the damn for a flood of feelings that rarely saw the light of day. Like an underground river, his feelings tended to rush and tumble and bubble just beneath the surface, eroding the rock and hardpacked soil that hid the torrents from the casual eye.

Do I like myself? Why or why not?

I can think of a lot of reasons why not! Certainly a lot more "why nots" than "whys." And that's not all—I'm so fed up with family, friends, school, Christianity. It would be so much easier to run away and live a wicked life of sin. But I can't. Some of my values and priorities are hidden under confusion and hurt, but they're still there and I know I must abide by them.

Fifteen minutes before the main service began in the sanctuary, the pastor resumed his position behind the podium and cleared his throat.

"Everyone pass your questionnaire to the aisle to be picked up. You don't have to sign your name if you don't want to, but the sheets will help us know what areas to focus on in the next couple of weeks as we study Bible passages and learn how to see ourselves the way God sees us. Remember, we can't structure the class to meet your needs unless we know what they are."

Papers passed over Scott's lap, but he didn't add his to the stack. Instead, he grabbed it in the center and crumpled it into a tight ball. He dropped it in a trash can as he walked out the door.

The clock on the microwave glowed 12:39 as Scott heard the engine of his parents' car roar into the driveway and then idle into silence. A moment later keys jingled on the porch, and then the front door swung open.

"Hi, sweetie. Good morning at church?" Gail asked as she walked into the living room. Chuck held the screen door open for her with one hand and tossed his Bible on the credenza with the other. He cocked his head to see what Scott was watching on TV.

"Yeah. Fine, mom," Scott replied without glancing up from where he sprawled on the couch. A Pepsi and a bag of potato chips lay on the floor next to him.

"You beat us home," Gail said. "Didn't you stay for the church service?"

"Nah, I just went to Sunday school." He reached for the remote control and punched the volume button up. His eyes still hadn't left the TV screen.

"Why's that?" she asked.

"Oh, I was feeling a little tired," he lied, memories of Marty's rumor . . . of the questionnaire . . . of his confusion . . . still lodged, unwanted, in his head. "I just felt like coming home."

"Is that your soap opera you're watching again?" Chuck asked.

"Yeah, *Ryan's Hope.* I taped the shows I missed this week."

Gail walked into the kitchen and poured herself a glass of iced tea. She took a sip as she walked back into the living room. She looked at the TV with a hand on her hip. "By the way, Scott, did you have a chance to go job hunting this week?"

"Well, actually, no." His eyes met hers for the first time. "I had finals, remember? I'll go next week."

"I thought we agreed it would be best to start looking before school lets out."

"Mom, I'm trying to watch this, okay?" His voice was sharp, biting. "I've had a few things on my mind lately. I haven't had the time or the energy!"

"You've had the time and the energy to watch soap operas," Gail snapped. "You've had the time and the energy to drive up to Hollywood to see movies. Sometimes I'm just not sure where your priorities are."

Scott got up from the couch and turned off the TV with a slap of his hand. He brushed by Gail without looking at her and shut his bedroom door. He lay on his bed with arms crossed over his eyes. *Nobody understands me,* he thought. Colors streamed into the blackness as he rubbed his eyelids with his palms. *I'm trying to grow up, but I'm having trouble. Mom and Dad want me to be perfect, but I'm not. I have faults—many of them. Mom doesn't understand this.*

And I hope she never does. I don't want her to ever know the things I'm going through.

Three weeks later, on a muggy day, a blue VW bug rumbled into Scott's driveway. Out jumped Kirk Graham, togged in a red tank-top and grey swimsuit. On the lawn next door, four drenched kids playing with a garden hose pointed at Kirk and whispered to each other. The kids inched forward side by side like a fierce advancing army with artillery in hand. They came to a halt as Kirk stopped and turned toward them. "Don't squirt me, but you can squirt Scott when we come out, okay?" he bargained. The hose battalion erupted in laughter.

Scott met Kirk at the front door. The summer sun had streaked Scott's auburn hair with highlights. He wore a light blue Hang Ten swimsuit, thongs, and a T-shirt.

"Great day for the beach, buddy," Kirk said. "Let's hit it."

"Right on, slick," Scott returned, grabbing his towel and cooler. Kirk pointed to the neighbor's yard and offered a quiet warning; the two sprinted toward the car to avoid the stream of water that came from behind the waist-high hedge.

They arrived at the beach twenty minutes later, smoothed their towels on the sand, peeled off their shirts, and dashed toward the water. Kirk plunged head first into the white foamy surf while Scott stopped at the water's edge to watch his friend swim out. Kirk beckoned him with a wave and a yell, and Scott, too, dove beneath a crashing wave. The next several hours were spent alternately swimming, lying in the sun, drinking Pepsi, and talking. The friends exchanged thoughts and ideas about people in the church college group, old high school friends, plans for the future, and family pressures.

Hours later the two sat, smelling of saltwater, in Kirk's VW in the driveway of Scott's house. A gentle breeze gusted through the open car window and blew strings of sun-dried blond hair into Kirk's eyes. He ran his fingers through the strands, brushing them out of his eyes. The hair remained interwoven in his fingers as his elbow rested on the steering wheel. He glanced at Scott, whose face displayed the effects of the searing sun on a pale complexion. Scott's nose beamed as if he'd just come in from the cold. His forehead was a strip of red paint.

"Looks like you got some serious sun," Kirk said.

Scott gave a lazy nod.

Kirk continued. "I've been thinking about something you said earlier today, you know, about feeling like you can't really talk to anyone."

"Yeah?" Scott acknowledged.

"I think everybody feels that way sometimes."

"I don't know," Scott said honestly.

"I know *I* feel that way sometimes. Just maybe . . . maybe not as much as you do." Kirk spoke slowly, puzzling out the words as they came. "We're different there I think."

"How?"

"You come across really . . . well, crazy."

"Crazy?" Scott repeated.

"In a good way. Like you just like to have fun," Kirk said, then shrugged. "You're a blast at all the church socials, school parties, whatever."

"And that makes us different?"

"No, not that part. The other part. The serious side. There's a part of you that's a real loner. You think . . . and feel . . . a lot more deeply than a lot of people. And certainly a lot more deeply than you let on."

Scott stared across at his friend for a moment. "You sound surprised."

"Not surprised really. Well, maybe a little. Let's just say I'm glad to know both sides of Scott Cameron. And Scott. . . ."

"Yeah?"

"About not having anyone to talk to."

"Yes?"

"You can always count on me. I want to be there for you. You know, to listen. You're a good friend. I just wanted you to know that."

Later, as Kirk's VW pulled out of the driveway, Scott sat on the front porch, swatting his calves and feet with the towel to brush away the clinging sand. He stopped and rested his elbows on his knees. A cool breeze swirled around his feet and he watched as wisps of sand were blown into the flower bed. He looked up and his eyes locked onto a solitary bird flying across the cool blue twilight sky.

On a Sunday night several weeks later, Scott let himself in the front door, home from the evening service at church. Neither his parents nor Tammy were home yet. He circled the kitchen table on his way to the battered Frigidaire, grabbed an orange from the second shelf, and kicked the fridge door shut with his foot. On the way to his bedroom he tossed the fruit into the air. It spun toward the ceiling; he caught it easily on the way back down.

In his room, Scott pulled a comic book from his collection, set the orange on the nightstand, and sprawled on the bed, thumbing through the first couple of pages. But he was too full, too blessed to waste the moment on Captain Leero.

Scott tossed the comic aside and grabbed his journal. Something special was happening to him that summer, and he didn't want to forget a minute of it. He grabbed a pen and began scrawling onto a page half-filled with a previous entry.

Tonight at church was very meaningful. After church we had a foot washing ceremony. It's to demonstrate our servanthood

*and humility to others like Christ did to His disciples when He
washed their feet, dusty from all their travels.*

*Anyway, I was in the gym with hundreds of people won-
dering whose feet I'd be washing when Kirk Graham came up
behind me and said he wanted to wash my feet. He said he'd
been looking for me for fifteen minutes. He made a special effort
to find me. He even said, "I wanted to wash your feet because I
really care about you, and this is a good way to show it." What
a friend! And I really care about him too.*

After all the loneliness.

After all the hurt over Paul Reardon. . . .

*After all the "just misses" with girls like Wendy Dolen and
even Colleen from Western Christian. . . .*

I think it's finally happening.

*I think I'm finally going to get the very best friend I've been
longing for ever since I can remember.*

Summer vacation was drawing to a close. Scott slammed
the wooden gate behind him and negotiated the moss-covered
stepping stones that led the way into Kirk's back yard. He threw
his towel and keys on a lawn chair and joined his friend at the
barbecue grill.

"I was wondering when you'd get here," Kirk said with a
chuckle. "I was ready to eat this hamburger raw."

"Yeah, sorry. Got off work a little late. The other waiter was
late getting there to take over my shift. Then the dinner crowd
started coming. Anyway, I'm here now, and I'm hungry."

"Good. 'Cause I got enough hamburgers to make you sink to
the bottom of the pool." Kirk plopped two hunks of meat on the
grill where they sizzled and steamed. Kirk and Scott sat on nylon-
mesh chairs beneath an umbrella-topped table. The fringes of
the umbrella cast a shadowy pattern on the table. Kirk reached
for a bag of chips and ripped it open.

"I made my plane reservations yesterday," Kirk said. "This
time next month, I'll be back in some humid college classroom
in Indiana."

"I thought you already had that taken care of." Scott's hand groped for the chips, his eyes never leaving Kirk's.

"Nope. You're lucky to be going to Western Christian. It's close. You don't have all that expensive plane travel to worry about."

"Yeah, well, I'm thinking of switching schools."

"No kidding. Why?"

"Not because I don't love it there—I do. In fact, being at Western is like . . ." Scott paused to think. "It's like I'm growing spiritually for the first time in a long time. I really dread what it'll be like to go to a school without all the great chapels and Christian teachers and friends and stuff."

"So, why quit?"

Scott shrugged. "It's finances. My part-time job at Polly's Restaurant doesn't do much toward tuition at a private college. I thought I'd take in a year or so at a city college, maybe live at home awhile."

"That makes sense."

"Anyway, you're right. Either way I'll still be going back to school in the area. No plane trips for me." Scott fell quiet for a moment. "You go back to college in three weeks, huh?" Kirk nodded. Scott added, "Man, I'm going to miss you."

"I know. It's been a great summer. We've had a lot of fun. The beach, Dodger game, church camp. But hey, it ain't over yet!" Kirk stood and peeked beneath the hamburger patty with a spatula. He flipped it over and the sizzle began again.

"I don't know what I'm going to do when you're gone," Scott said, shielding his eyes from the sun with his hand as he looked up at Kirk.

"What do you mean? It'll be fine," Kirk said over his shoulder as he faced the barbecue. "We can write and stuff. And I'll be back at Christmas, maybe even Thanksgiving."

"Yeah . . . I guess so." Scott set down the potato chip in his hand. He stared at the pool as the sun shimmered on its undulating ripples. He broke his stare and glanced toward Kirk whose back was still turned. Scott's eyes riveted on Kirk's back as if he had x-ray vision. Kirk started to turn; Scott lowered his eyes. "Yeah," Scott mumbled, "I guess we can write and stuff."

Three weeks later, on a lazy Thursday afternoon, Scott

powered up the VCR and popped in a cassette of *Ryan's Hope*
segments. Every few minutes, however, he checked his wrist-
watch or glanced toward the front door. When the doorbell
finally rang, Scott stretched, peeled himself off the couch, and
aimed the remote at the TV. The tape whirred to a stop, and
the screen went to static. Scott slapped the TV off on his way
to the door.

He cracked the door open just in time to see the tail lights of
a blue VW retreating down the street. Scott's heart sank somewhere near his liver. On the welcome mat at his feet sat a gift-
wrapped box with a card. Cradling the package with both hands,
Scott headed toward his room. He ripped the paper, opened the
box, and pulled out a woodcarving of an eagle with wings spread
in flight. Then he opened the card:

> Dear Scott,
>
> Sorry I couldn't stay and say goodbye in person,
> but you know I've got to say *adios* to the family and
> catch my plane. Going away to college is tough, and
> it's even tougher having to say goodbye to a good friend
> like you.
>
> I bought this eagle with you in mind. To me the
> eagle represents strength and boldness. It is not afraid
> to fly at great heights because of its inward confidence
> and strength. The Old Testament says God brought the
> children of Israel out of Egypt and to Himself on "eagle's
> wings."
>
> Just as the children of Israel did, we need to trust in
> God who delivers us out of trials, temptations, loneliness,
> and insecurity. The eagle explores new areas without fear
> because of the strength within. Many times it flies alone
> and is content in just that.
>
> Scott, when you look at this eagle, think of boldness.
> Ask God to help you come out of yourself and laugh and
> be friendly and love without fear; for love in its true form
> is always right in the sight of God. This little eagle is just a
> token of my love, but it carries with it a depth of meaning.

I'll be sure to write while I'm away!
Your friend, Kirk.

Scott again picked up the eagle. After several minutes, he set it on his bookshelf, backed away from it, and stood staring at it from across the room.

Despite his disappointment that Kirk hadn't said goodbye in person, the corners of Scott's mouth turned up slowly in a smile that welled from the depths of his heart and lit up his entire countenance.

Why should he be so lucky?

Sure, he'd cared for people before; but for the first time that struck a conscious chord, someone—other than a family member—was loving Scott back. And for the first time in a long time, Scott felt good about himself, knowing that the faith of a friend had awarded him the greatest gift of all: the chance to have faith in himself.

If someone as great as Kirk loves me, then I must have some good qualities, Scott assured himself. *I'll think twice before I ever look down on myself again. And I won't make a mockery of Kirk's faith in me: I won't let Kirk or God down.*

I'll make them both proud of me yet!

Yet a couple weeks later, Scott wasn't so sure . . . that Kirk cared, that God cared, or that Scott possessed the power to make *anyone* proud of him.

It was Saturday morning. Gail and Chuck were running errands, and Tammy was at cheerleading practice. Scott sat alone in front of the television with the remote control in his hands. He flipped the channels around the dial and finally clicked the set off. He stood up and looked out the window at the mailbox—but the mailman had not yet come. Not that it mattered; in more than two weeks, Kirk Graham hadn't written once.

Scott finally meandered to the kitchen, grabbed some crackers out of a box on the white tile counter, and sat down at the kitchen table. He thumbed through the newspaper quickly, pausing long enough to read the entertainment section and

Dear Abby. He grabbed more crackers and walked into his room where he sat down at his desk with his journal.

But few words came.

What was there to say? Words were hardly adequate to capture and contain the hurt.

Scott's loneliness was simply overwhelming. Gut-wrenching. Heart-wringing. It was about as tangible as a soupy fog—dense and white and curling with the midnight breezes—converging on a dark and twisted ribbon of highway. About as tangible . . . and as dangerous, too.

Several weeks later, as the days cooled into October, there was still no word from Kirk Graham.

One night just after dinner Scott, restless, climbed into his Maverick. A cold wind blew against his face as he rolled down the car window to adjust the rear-view mirror. Twenty miles later, the Maverick crawled along a dimly-lit street as a faint siren echoed in the distance. Papers and aluminum cans twisted and swirled in the gutters. Blinking red-neon lights reflected against the windshield, intermittently illuminating the hazy glow that surrounded Scott's car.

Scott parked the car, wrestled into his denim jacket, and glanced around before opening the door. Scott had been here a dozen times, but this was the first time he'd come alone. He slipped two quarters into the meter and scurried toward the ticket window of the Harlequin theater in downtown Hollywood. "One for *Mutiny on the Bounty* please," he told a bored attendant, slipping a five dollar bill through the hole in the window.

Once inside the darkened theater, he chose an empty aisle—one of many—and slipped into one of the velvet-cushioned seats. Soon the projector lights flickered against the screen, and Scott shuffled out of his jacket and settled in to watch the film. Within seconds, Scott had escaped into the adventurous world he saw before him.

As the credits rolled two hours later, Scott waited for most of the small crowd to exit before he readied himself to leave. Outside in the chilly October night, he pulled on his jacket, falling in behind four men who had left the theater in front of him.

Scott looked down to zip his jacket against the wind. He looked back up in time to see two of the men clasp hands. The other two wrapped their arms around each other. Scott jerked to a halt. He let out a gasp. One of the men heard the sound, looked back at Scott, and laughed. The foursome kept walking.

Scott stood frozen in the misty night until the men disappeared from sight.

Arriving back home, Scott closed and locked his bedroom door, then collapsed onto his bed and buried his face in his arms. He wanted to forget what he'd seen . . . and yet the memory clung to him like the stale smoke of a cigarette.

A half hour passed, then an hour.

He couldn't clear the memory. And worse, he couldn't shake the feelings that the memory evoked. He was repulsed. Revolted. Shaken to his very core.

But like the queen in Shakespeare's *Hamlet*, Scott knew he protested too much. Finally he reached for his journal, cracked it open, and began to write:

As I was leaving the theater tonight, the four men in front of me hugged and touched each other—and it was obviously more than a gesture of companionship. I was so stunned. I felt like screaming. It was a hideous sight! It looked so—for the lack of a better term—queer. Needless to say, I was glad when I was back in the car and on my way home.

I feel sick about this evening, and appalled. I want to wrap myself in God's love—He's the only one who can save me.

Scott had hoped the transfer of his thoughts onto paper might release the pressure of the secret fears—it wouldn't be the first time that his pen had pulled off such a miracle. But that night, as he slipped into a pair of sweats, threw back the blankets, and crawled between the sheets, he did so with his secrets still boiling and steaming and bubbling painfully within.

He turned off the light with a shaky hand and stared up into the blackness. For the next three hours, he tossed and turned and tossed again. When the gray envelope of sleep finally overtook him, he continued to writhe and toss.

The dreams that followed were not kind. Blinding lights flashed. Whispers and screams collided. Fear twisted and wrenched his stomach. Thunder crashed and echoed, crashed and echoed. Hands clawed at nothing, and shadowy figures lurked. Pain burned. Contorted faces laughed.

Scott awoke the next morning and slumped on the edge of his bed. He rubbed his eyes and massaged his temples. He let out a low groan as he stood to his feet. After a wobbly shave and shower, Scott stumbled into the kitchen.

"Hi, sweetie, how'd you sleep?" Gail said brightly.

"Don't ask," Scott mumbled.

"I didn't hear you come in, son," Chuck remarked. "What time did you get in?"

"Don't ask."

"How 'bout some breakfast?" Gail asked. Scott stared out the window, oblivious to his mother's question. She spoke to him again a little louder. "Scott, would you like anything for breakfast?"

"Huh? Oh, maybe just some toast." He ate half a piece of toast while staring out the window.

"Scott, don't forget you need to take Tammy to the dentist this afternoon," Chuck reminded.

"Dentist? What dentist?" Scott repeated.

"Dr. Harrison. At 3:30. Did you forget?"

"Oh . . . no, I remember," Scott said. "Yeah, I'll take her."

Scott lumbered into his room and returned with a textbook, setting it next to the stack already on the table. He grabbed a brown-paper lunch bag out of the refrigerator and took another bite of his toast.

"I'm taking off for school," he said to Gail, who was standing at the sink rinsing dishes. "See you later, Dad," he yelled to the bedroom where Chuck had just retreated to brush his teeth. Scott picked up the stack of books. Moments later, the screen door slammed behind him.

Gail turned off the water faucet and reached for a sponge. As she wiped crumbs from the table, she spotted Scott's textbook lying on the table where he had set it down. She grabbed it and ran to the door. Too late. Scott had already driven away. She carried the book to Scott's room, set it on his desk, and turned to go.

Just inches from the textbook laid a notebook, open to a page that contained a single line. The words were roughly scrawled:

I made a secret commitment to God this morning. I can't discuss it, but it's very important.

Three weeks later—the day before Thanksgiving—Scott checked the mail for anything from Kirk. He stood by the front door, flipping through the junk mail and bills, but came up empty-handed as usual. Gail, baking pies in the kitchen, looked up as she heard the door to Scott's room close with a heavy thud. She paused, up her to wrists in dough, and listened. There were no new sounds, and the house settled quickly back into quiet. Then she heard the muffled strains of Scott's radio. She shrugged and turned back to the sticky dough.

Around four o'clock the following afternoon, empty pie pans soaked in dishwater in the kitchen sink. The refrigerator had been stocked with leftover turkey and trimmings, and the family's dishwasher was humming and churning away.

Outside, dark billowy clouds leaked small drops of rain on Scott's car as he stopped at a red light. An old woman wearing a floppy orange hat and a brown patched jacket pushed a grocery cart full of bags, blankets, and a suitcase tied shut with twine. Scott watched as she walked from one end of the crosswalk to the other. Scott turned his gaze toward his grandfather who slumped against the passenger door, his hands limp between his knees, his belly filled with Gail's best Thanksgiving dinner ever. The old man's head bobbed and lifted every few minutes as he fought a losing battle with sleep. Tufts of shaggy gray hair brushed and bristled against his collar.

Spray-painted graffiti scarred brick walls and apartment buildings. Coasting to a stop in front of a stop sign riddled with bullet holes, Scott tapped his grandfather on the leg. "Hmm, what?" Grandpa jerked awake.

"We're almost there, Grandpa," Scott said.

"Yes, yes, I can see," the old man said in a gravelly voice. He pressed two fingers against his temple and emitted a small moan.

"You okay, Grandpa?" Scott's eyes darted back and forth between his grandfather and the road. The old man grunted and leaned his head against the window. He was silent for a few moments until a jolting cough rocked his body. An eruption of hacks burst from his lungs. He then slumped down again with forehead pressed against the window.

The car stopped, and Scott helped his grandfather step up the curb. An arm around the waist steadied the old man's unbalanced gait. Each of the twenty-two stairs leading to apartment G seemed a mountain to climb. Finally, Grandpa was back in the dank one-bedroom apartment that no member of the family had been able to persuade him to give up.

Driving home along the black streets and slick pavement, Scott's memory flipped through pages of his childhood photo album: Grandpa carving the annual Thanksgiving turkey; sleeping over at Grandma and Grandpa's house; being slipped silver dollars for no particular reason; Scott and Grandpa taking Sparkle for walks in the park together; sitting on Grandpa's knee and listening wide-eyed to adventure stories. The glowing reverie was doused by the image of his grandfather tonight.

Scott had seen his grandfather in bad shape before . . . but not like that night. It was tragic to see a life destroyed by alcohol, tragic to watch a man lured to his death by a deadly obsession. In Scott's eye, his grandfather once had it all: life, health, and the love of family and friends. Yet he had risked it all in return for . . . what?

Scott wished he had the courage to ask his grandfather if it had been worth the trade. But maybe Scott knew the answer after all.

Weeks later, Scott sat amid heaps of Christmas wrapping paper, bows and ribbon, Styrofoam packing, and boxes. The paper and boxes rose like small mountains around the tinsel-strung Christmas tree. Twinkling Christmas tree lights reflected against the window, and cassette-deck carols drifted softly through the living room. Keeping with tradition, Tammy had turned Sparkle into the "bow monster" with a hundred bows stuck to her fur. Gail walked in from the kitchen with a garbage bag in hand. She looked over the room, sighed, and stooped to pick up a handful of crumpled paper.

"Honey, why don't you relax?" Chuck suggested. "Enjoy the yuletide mess for a while."

"All right, I will," Gail said, dropping the green bag where she stood. "After I get some coffee, that is. Anyone else for some coffee or hot chocolate? Scott?"

Scott looked up from the floor where he was thumbing through the *100 Years of Hollywood* book he got from Tammy. He lay on his stomach, head resting on his hands. He looked up at his mom like a rheumy-eyed puppy.

"Nothing for me, thanks." Scott put his forehead down on his hands and closed his eyes. Chuck leafed through a new book, while Tammy headed to the bathroom with a new dress in hand.

"Is anything wrong, Scott?" Gail asked, walking back into the room, mug in hand.

"No, I'm just thinking," he said with his head buried in his palms.

"What about, son?" Chuck asked.

"Nothing."

"Sweetie, I heard your friend Kirk Graham is back in town. Why don't you give him a call?"

"I don't know. I haven't heard from him for months. I feel a little funny."

"Oh, go on. It's Christmas. I'm sure he'd appreciate it."

"Okay, maybe." He lay still for a few moments, then pushed himself off the floor. "Thanks again for a great Christmas." He gathered an armful of presents and walked into his room. He dropped them on the desk and dropped himself on his bed.

Call him, they said?

Call *Kirk?*

In the semester Kirk had been away at school, Scott had written six letters . . . and received zero in reply. Kirk had been home from college for a week and a half . . . and Scott had yet to hear from his friend. The depression that had settled into Scott's bones with the first onslaught of cool weather began to feel overwhelming.

Scott glanced toward the eagle statue on the bookshelf. He shifted to face it, then jumped from the bed and took it in his hands. His eyes pored over every cut, every edge, every curve. He set it down and backed away slowly, still staring at it. He reached for his journal and flipped back to the letter from Kirk that had been attached to the eagle. He skipped several lines, then stopped to read: "To me the eagle represents strength and boldness. . . . The eagle explores new areas without fear because of the strength within. Many times it flies alone and is content in just that."

Scott wasn't sure he was an eagle, after all. He wasn't sure he was cut out to fly alone. He flipped the journal forward to a blank page, sat down at the desk and began to write:

The year is nearly at its end. I survived my first semester at the public college, away from Western and all the good influence that was there. All in all, I've had some good times and some bad times. I've had my share of struggles—deep, deep struggles. I've learned a lot.

Scott stopped and capped his pen. He thought for a moment, then closed the notebook. He stared at the cover. Finally, he cracked it open again and picked up his pen. His hand trembled a little as the words appeared:

But to be very honest, there are some things in my life that disgust and terrify me. Hopefully, with the Lord's help, I can overcome them .
   . . before they overcome me.

FIVE

The Dark Descent Begins

G ail sat at the kitchen table, one leg tucked beneath her, correcting the math tests her third graders had handed in just before Christmas break. Behind her, a pot of stew bubbled on the stove. The aroma of banana-nut bread spilled from the hot oven.

"Mom, I'm going," Scott yelled in transit. The words started at his bedroom and ended somewhere near the front door. Keys jangled in hand.

"*You're* sure in a hurry!" Gail hollered back. She unfolded her leg to get up just as Scott stuck his head in the doorway.

"Don't get up, Mom. I'm fine. I just need to get away for a while." He looked past her toward the sights and smells of dinner. "And don't worry, I won't be long."

"That's the least of my worries," she answered, a slight furrow in her brow. "This is Christmas break, remember? You're supposed to have fun. Relax."

"I am relaxing. And I'm having fun, honest. Maybe I'll go to the library, browse a little. Maybe look up a couple old movie reviews."

"Well, that'll be nice."

"Yeah. There's nothing *else* to do."

"Oh?" Gail raised an eyebrow.

"Anyway, I'll be back by dinner." Scott turned to leave.

"Scott?"

"Yeah?"

"Did you ever call Kirk back? I left a note on your desk."

"Oh, that. I called. He wasn't home. Busy guy, that Kirk," Scott said dryly. He flashed his hand in a brief wave. "See you later, Mom."

Gail stared into the empty doorway long after the crown of red hair was gone and the roar of the engine in the driveway had faded into the distance.

Deep in the catacombs of the city library, Scott slumped at a stained wood table strewn with thick, dusty volumes of antique magazines. *Life*, 1933 to 1934. *The Saturday Evening Post*, 1925 to 1926. *Good Housekeeping*, 1942 to 1943. He had managed to find a number of old movie reviews for some of his favorite classics. He even photocopied one article for Tammy.

Now he slumped, staring blindly at the books before him.

"Psssst."

Scott still slumped and stared.

"Pssssst!"

A paper wad sailed through the air and pinged Scott above the left ear. He jumped, then turned angrily.

Several desks away, three girls were watching him. One shrugged an apology. "I don't want to be rude," she whispered loudly, "but you're driving me crazy."

"I'm *what?*"

"The tapping."

"What tapping?"

"Your *pencil.* You've been tapping your pencil on the desk for the past fifteen minutes. It's driving us nuts."

Scott looked down at the pencil in his hand. His face reddened. "I . . . I didn't know. . . . I'm sorry."

The girls giggled.

Scott pushed his chair from the table with a screech. The girls laughed again. He escaped into the stacks of bound magazines.

He roamed, restless, for a while, pulling volumes here and there and flipping through the pages absentmindedly. It was nearly five o'clock, but he couldn't go home quite yet. There was too much to sort out. He needed space. And quiet.

But something told him he could be on the moon and he'd still feel crowded on the inside. He could be on silent Mars and still be deafened by the clash of conflict within.

Scott tried to shake the thoughts away. He was standing along the back wall of the stacks, next to a small study table. A couple of broken pencils and a magazine lay discarded by the last occupant.

Something caught Scott's eye, and he reached for the magazine.

He let out a low whistle. He could hardly believe his eyes . . . in a public library, no less! His heart pounded double time as he slowly peeled back the cover. He swallowed hard. He flashed a furtive glance behind him into the stacks. But no one was watching. He stared back down at the magazine in his hands. He gulped and turned another page.

An hour later, Scott moved to set the magazine back down on the table. But his hand stopped mid-air. He hesitated just a moment before flipping to the back of the magazine and skimming the ad pages there. He found the page he was looking for, tore it quickly from its binding, and stuffed it in his pocket.

In the following week, Scott reached Kirk by phone. Two days later, the friends finally got together for Coke and some small talk at Kirk's parents' home. They were joined by several other buddies from church, who laughed and joked and vied for the attention of their visiting friend. Listening to the banter, Scott remembered the undivided attention he once got from Kirk. He remembered the six unanswered letters he had written this past semester. He remembered the eagle. Scott suspected he was being overly sensitive. But he wasn't sure. And even if he *were* overreacting, he didn't know how to stop the pain he felt.

At 9:30, Scott grabbed his coat and announced he had to get home to his books.

Kirk walked him to the door. There was an awkward silence, for just a moment, between the friends. "You okay, Scott? You were really quiet tonight."

"I'm fine. Just fine. It's just . . . well . . . you know how classes are."

"Sure. But your classes haven't started back up yet, have they?"

"Uh, no. But we start back in four days."

"That's too bad," Kirk said. "You know I don't have to fly back for a couple more weeks. I guess we're on a different schedule than you guys. So I'll be around a little while longer."

"Well, like I said, I want to be ready. I'm reading ahead."

"If you say so." Kirk studied his friend. "Hey, Scott, I'm sorry we didn't get more time to talk in the last couple weeks, but time goes by real fast when you've got Christmas and family and all that. . . ."

"I understand."

"Really?"

"Oh, more than you realize," Scott said dryly.

"We'll get together and talk before I go, okay?"

"Sure, Kirk." Scott reached for the door. "Sure we will."

It was a damp Monday morning in January, a week into the new semester. The classroom twittered with small talk as students swapped weekend updates in the last few moments before class began. Scott made his way through the aisle and dropped himself in his seat. He pulled off his jacket, wet from the rain, and slung it over the back of his chair.

Scott turned as someone tapped him on the shoulder. It was Rosemary. She had attended high school with Scott, and now they shared a class, "Religious Ethics," at City College. She handed Scott a newspaper clipping and flashed him a smile.

"Bet you didn't know we went to school with such a celeb," she said, standing next to his desk.

"Who's that?" He took the clipping and skimmed the first paragraph. His eyes narrowed. He looked back up at Rosemary, his lips pressed into a thin line.

"Isn't that great, Scott? I cut it out for you 'cause I know you guys are really good friends."

"That was real thoughtful of you."

"You hadn't seen it or anything, had you?" Rosemary asked.

"No."

"Well, that's good. It's all about how he and his brother, plus his cousin, plus his uncle, *plus* his grandfather all made Eagle Scout. That's five people from the same family—three generations even—all getting the top award in the Boy Scouts. It's really interesting." She glanced toward the front of the classroom where the teacher had just arrived and stood arranging his notes. "Gotta go. No, no, keep it. I already read it this morning." She waved Scott's hand aside and hurried back to her seat.

As Dr. Strickland launched into his lecture from the podium, Scott eyed the article once more. The first line was the real sticker:

> The name Graham soars as high as the eagle in local Boy Scout circles. No, we'd better make that five eagles, for that's the aerie the family of C. Waldon Graham has produced since he helped found Troop 22 back in 1949.

"Kirk and his eagles," Scott muttered beneath his breath, skimming ahead to where his friend was named as one of the family's five Eagle Scouts. Scott shook his head. *I guess what he said was true—eagles do soar alone. They don't need friends. Not even another eagle. He certainly doesn't need me.*

Scott's thoughts were interrupted by Dr. Strickland's voice fading in: ". . . he feels God wants him to be that way. He sees no conflict with being a Christian and with being homosexual. Yes, Rosemary?"

Scott's heart leaped into hyperpulse. He could barely hear Rosemary's answer over the pounding in his ears.

"I don't buy that, Dr. Strickland. I believe what the Bible says. It's really clear on homosexuality. You know, how it's wrong and everything. There's no way you can believe in God and think you're gay at the same time."

"The Bible?" blurted a guy in the back with close-cropped brown hair. "That may have been fine way back when, but times have changed. I say anything goes, as long as you don't hurt other people. And a lot of religions today are beginning to reflect the same kind of thinking. You know. Live and let live."

"Any other comments?" Dr. Strickland scanned the class. Scott stared down at the desk, praying he wouldn't be called on to comment.

A jock from the basketball team raised his hand. "Okay, let's go with the Christian thing for a minute. Let's say some guy really does get off thinking about other guys. A lot of people control themselves and don't have sex till they're married. Of course, not everybody waits. . . ." He flashed a winsome smile. Several people in the class giggled. "Anyway, I don't see why a homo can't control his lusts the same way. I mean, just don't *do* it."

The opinions ricocheted back and forth. Could a man love God and lust after men? Forty minutes later Scott left the classroom. The article about Kirk and his family was still clutched in one hand, but nearly forgotten.

Later that night, when the house fell silent and Gail, Chuck, and Tammy had gone to bed, Scott lay awake in the dark, staring at the ceiling. He finally flipped to his stomach and groped under the bed. He pulled out a notebook.

By the light of a winter moon, Scott began to write.

I feel that a person can most certainly be both a Christian and a homosexual—after all, it's certainly no sin to be tempted. I do feel, however, that homosexuality is wrong, and that God is very definite on that. I condemn the sin, but I don't condemn the sinner. Today in my religious ethics class, one guy brought up the idea that homosexuals should be able to be patient and not have sex, just like other people wait to have sex till they're married. Well, that sounds very nice, but I think it's easier said than done. After all, the Christian homosexual should know there isn't much chance of his getting married.

I don't know anybody personally who is a Christian homosexual.

But if I did—or if it were I—I can imagine how much hurting would go on inside. I would try to live a pure life, and be so

rooted in the Lord that I could control myself. I'd try to remember
that this world will all pass away, and that the things I do now
will have an influence on the way my life will be in eternity. I
would force myself to be strong.

Two days later, Scott stood in a phone booth just outside the
college library. His hands trembled as he opened his wallet and
extracted a piece of paper. It was dog-eared and wrinkled from a
month in his pocket, and a ragged edge showed where it had been
torn from a magazine. The many folds and creases made some of
the ads difficult to read; however, the tag line at the bottom of
the page was still legible. It read, *After Dark: The entertainment*
magazine for the Los Angeles gay community. Scott hesitated,
then dropped in his quarter. Taking a deep breath, he dialed the
Gay Hotline advertised on the paper he gripped in his hand.

The very next night, Scott drove his Maverick seventeen miles
into Anaheim, the home of Disneyland, America's favorite play-
ground. He drove right past the great park for children of all ages.
the pinnacle of the Matterhorn, jutting skyward, could be seen
from the freeway. It appeared briefly, then disappeared, as Scott
sped onward in the dark.

He exited the freeway several miles down the road into an
affluent part of town. Following directions scribbled on the back
of an envelope, Scott wove through unfamiliar streets, finally
slowing in front of a windowless, mauve building marked by
flashing blue-neon lights. He circled several times, finally seek-
ing out the darkest corner of the parking lot. It was a quarter
filled with cars of every make and year. He parked behind a silver
Volvo and carefully locked his car. Turning up his jacket collar,
he hurried across the lot toward a back door invisible from the
street beyond, yet lit by the flashing blue-neon sign. He paused
for a moment at the threshold, frozen in the throbbing blue light.
Then his hand darted from his jacket pocket. He gripped the door
handle, hard, and slipped inside.

SIX

To Hell and Back

The next morning, in Friday's American Lit class, the pre-class murmur was in full throttle as students compared plans for the weekend. Yet the scattered phrases faded in and out of Scott's brain like a car radio passing between the mountains.

Scott slumped in his chair and looked out the second story window at the dark clouds blanketing the sky. His eyes were riveted on the raindrops that began to drum against the window.

An hour later, the professor dismissed the class and students swarmed toward the door. Scott startled out of his vacant stare. He glanced around and then down at the notebook paper in front of him—it was empty except for some doodles of rain clouds and lightening.

The hours passed. Meaningless. Insignificant. Unmarked by anyone . . . anything . . . except the numbness that welled up, out of and over Scott until he felt buried alive in the dull throb emitting from his paralyzed soul.

Sometime after noon, Scott plopped his tray down on the cafeteria table next to his books. Bruce, a sophomore with collar length brown hair and a hockey player's face, followed right behind Scott. He slapped his tray on the table across from Scott's and grunted, "Hey, Scott, I owe you, buddy. I think our lunchtime lessons are paying off. I passed yesterday's quiz.

Thanks to you, I might even pass the class."

"Sure, no problem," Scott said flatly.

The cafeteria air vibrated with the chatter of a bustling lunchtime crowd. As Bruce leafed through notes on cell reproduction, Scott stared blankly into the spaghetti noodles that wove and knotted like macrame on his plate. He swallowed hard to dissolve the aching lump in his throat. It didn't budge.

Scott closed his eyes, wishing he were anywhere but here in this crowded, noisy, lonely cafeteria. If Bruce noticed, maybe he'd simply think Scott was praying over his food: a nice, *long* prayer.

Scott tried to picture his silent, familiar room at home. He envisioned himself lying on his bed, staring up at the stucco ceiling with its moon-like crags and craters. It was a quiet place . . . peaceful and safe . . . where someone could think . . . and figure things out . . . without interruption.

God, what have I done?

Scott was yanked back to reality by a slap on the shoulder.

"Did you hear me?" Bruce snorted.

Scott stared blankly at his friend.

"I said those chicks over there are checking us out. Let's go talk to 'em."

Scott groaned as Bruce dragged him up by one arm, hauling him deeper into the buzz and swirl of cafeteria clamor. If Scott could just, somehow, get through this day. . . .

Miles away on a quiet tree-lined street, a brick and stucco house sat empty. Inside, one of the bedroom doors was ajar. Inside that bedroom, the shades were drawn against the midday sun and dust settled silently on shelves lined with comic books. In the diffused sunlight, a wooden clock ticked out a hollow rhythm. Beside the clock sat a small brass key that opened the bottom left desk drawer. Inside the drawer, beneath two dog-eared copies of *Time* magazine, rested a journal. It contained a page with secret thoughts written in Scott's minuscule, yet certain print:

I hardly slept a wink two nights ago after I made the phone call. I felt sick, and my mind was too preoccupied with what I had heard on the phone.

Then, yesterday morning I struggled for hours. I could feel the Lord telling me what I should do, and I could hear Satan telling me what I thought I wanted to do—what was wrong to do. But I'm afraid I listened to Satan.

Each step of the way, I told myself, "Now this is as far as I'm going . . . just to satisfy my curiosity." But I kept going! By yesterday afternoon I had called the gay bath just to ask a few questions.

Then last night I took the final step.

I don't want to go into too much detail—it still makes me sick. But I want to write down some record of what happened, in the hopes that it will keep me from doing it again. If anybody ever reads this, I think I'll die—so I'll have to keep today's entry private . . . forever.

After paying and joining Club 2000 under the pseudonym Brian Johnson, I was shown around. There was a movie/TV room, sauna, steam room, showers, pool room, and quite a few bathrooms. I was there till 2:30 a.m. I met two guys, even though it wasn't very crowded. The first was John. He was gross. I desperately wanted to get out of the situation, but once I got started I was afraid to back out. Then there was George. George is in his thirties, but looks much younger. He just moved out here from New York and lives in a fancy condo in Seal Beach (he's quite rich). He wants me to visit him—often—as his frequent "lover." Not hardly! I may be stupid, but not that stupid!

I finally decided that I'd had enough, went to my locker, got dressed and left. I got home and felt ashamed and very, very ugly.

Why did I do it? Maybe because I was feeling so down on myself that I wanted to do something horrible. I still surprised myself though. I never thought I'd go that far. I can't believe it.

What did I get out of it? Not much pleasure—that's for sure. I didn't like it at all—being used and held as though I were an object. As ugly as it was though, the temptations are still there to go back again and again. How can I be like that? I know it's wrong. I know that my life has much more to offer than that. Why am I drawn to that?

Nobody knows — not my family or friends — so my secret is safe. But God knows and I know . . . and I'm having a hard time living with that right now.

"Did you enjoy church this morning, Scotty?" Gail asked brightly as she pulled the Sunday roast out of the oven.

Scott, leaning against the tile counter with his arms folded, stared down in silence at the fake grout lines in the linoleum.

He wished desperately he had the courage to tell the truth.

Thirty minutes earlier, as Gail and Tammy set the kitchen table, Scott had penned the truth in his carefully hidden journal:

At church this morning I felt like running up to the pulpit and screaming, "Help me!" I wanted to plead for help, but I just couldn't. I haven't even really been able to ask the Lord for help yet either.

Scott looked up at Gail. She was still waiting for his answer.

"Church?" He lied through a smile. "It was great. Just great, Mom."

During dinner, the family chatted about Tammy's upcoming history exam, the possibility of taking a vacation together next summer, Scott's job at Polly's Restaurant, the friends they had seen at church that morning.

And then the bomb fell. No one heard the whistle as it winged its way toward Scott's heart. No one felt the earth shake . . . except Scott. No one smelled the smoke, felt the fire, heard the screams. Except Scott.

"Scott, did you talk to Kirk today at church?" Tammy said casually. "He's going back to college tonight, you know."

"Really?" Scott looked up from his plate, his heart beating a tatoo against his ribs. "Are you sure he's leaving *tonight?*"

"Sure. I was standing right there when he was saying good-bye to everyone."

Scott stifled any possible reply by filling his mouth with a spoonful of mashed potatoes. He fell silent throughout the rest of the meal, nursing the wounds, hearing the sirens, burying the dead that no one else even knew were there.

After dinner, he retreated to his room to pick up where he left off in the journal, trying to make some sense out of the carnage that had once been his heart:

I don't really feel so well—physically as well as on the inside. Maybe it's guilt feelings. God knows I feel horribly guilty. And yet I don't know how to turn to God. There's a stone wall, a barrier between us.

Maybe it's because I'm secretly harboring thoughts of returning to the Club 2000 and doing the same thing again. I don't know what to do—it's a battle between what I should do and what I want to do.

And on top of everything else . . . Kirk is going back to college tonight and he didn't even say goodbye. He never even tried to get in touch with me. I feel bitter toward him—and angry at myself for trusting him. It hurts me so much. Oh, Lord, couldn't he have at least said goodbye?

I feel so awful about what I've done. I need to talk with somebody—desperately. But who? Certainly no one in my church college group. They call themselves a "family," but they are far from it. They can be so cliquish, so unfriendly. I need to lean on someone right now. I need to know I'm important and loved. I don't get that at church, not from anyone. Not that anyone could tell I was hurting, of course. I can be a good actor when I want to be.

I was very disappointed, almost bitter, when I left church this morning. At this point in my life, I probably need more Christian love and fellowship and understanding than ever before, but I am getting none. It's sad that after twenty years, there's no one that I can turn to . . . even if I had the guts to do so.

I'll admit, I'm not the best at telling people I'm really hurting. But can't they see?

Scott trudged through the next week in a dream-like blur. He went to his classes, work, and church, but a fog bleared the faces that scuttled in and out of his sight. The voices of friends and family echoed inside his head as if he were trapped in a giant cavern.

At the end of the week, Scott broke down and spent an hour on his knees, confessing everything to God and pleading for forgiveness and deliverance. When he finally stood, his face stained with tears, he dove straight for his wallet on his desk. Fumbling with the cellophane pockets, he managed to withdraw his membership card for the Club 2000. He tore it to shreds.

He felt . . . forgiven. As if Jesus Christ had welcomed him back into fellowship. In fact, Scott felt clean again . . . almost.

Although Scott knew God had forgiven him, he wasn't quite sure he could forgive himself.

And then there was the small matter of consequence.

Scott remembered a sermon preached at church in which the pastor pointed out that God's forgiveness eliminates the *punishment* of our sins . . . but not necessarily the *consequences*.

And later that morning, something happened that focused Scott's thoughts—and one of his journal entries—on just what those consequences might turn out to be:

I'm a bit frightened. When I went to the bathroom this morning it hurt. Of course, it could just be nerves. After all, I've been through a lot lately. But could it possibly be some sort of venereal disease?

Oh no, I suppose that's silly. That couldn't happen to me. Not the first time I ever. . . .

Well, I just won't think about it. I'm probably imagining things. Besides, the Lord is with me.

After two days of burning pain, Scott was certain something was wrong.

"Cooper, Scott." A stout nurse called from the doorway, peering at the clipboard in her hands. "Scott Cooper? Is there a Scott Cooper here?"

"Uh, yes, right here, ma'am," Scott answered. For a moment

he had forgotten he'd used a pseudonym. Scott walked toward the uniformed nurse, past several old men dozing in vinyl chairs and a couple of mothers holding crying babies and small children with bare feet. He walked with eyes averted and shoulders hunched forward, praying he wouldn't see anyone he knew.

Scott's regret over coming to the Public Health Clinic intensified with every step.

"Third room on the left," the nurse said blandly, looking past Scott toward the overflowing waiting room. "Someone will be with you in a few minutes."

During the twenty minute wait, Scott's mind rifled scattered thoughts and prayers. *I feel so alone—I should've had someone come with me, but how could I explain? . . . Dear God, how could I have gotten myself in this mess? . . . What if I see someone I know here? What will I say? . . . What if I do have V.D.? Then what? . . . Lord, I know You've forgiven me. Help me through this.*

A second nurse finally arrived with a clipboard and machine gunned Scott with questions: Have you ever had venereal disease before? Where did you contract it? What are the names of other people you may have infected? Finally, she put the clipboard down, drew a blood sample from Scott's arm, took cultures to be tested, and gave him a container of antibiotics. She instructed him to take one capsule every six hours and to drink a lot of water.

"I . . . I can go now?" Scott asked.

She shook her head, dashing his hopes. "Not yet. Follow me."

He was ushered across the hall, into a room with four other men sitting in front of a table. Scott slithered into one of the orange plastic chairs without looking into the eyes of the other men. Scott shifted his weight and picked at a fingernail as minutes passed in a thick silence. Soon a well-built black man in a white lab coat settled in behind the desk.

"You're all here for the same reason, so I won't bother talking to you individually." The man's low, sonorous voice saturated the antiseptic room. His eyes roved from face to face. "I'm going to give you instructions so you can avoid contracting venereal diseases in the future." As he talked, Scott's eyes were drawn to a ring on the man's finger. The ring bore the image of a fish, the symbol of Christian unity. Scott looked into the doctor's face for a hint of compassion. Somehow if Scott could tell him that he was a Christian, maybe the man would lend some support, some understanding, some empathy.

"Have any of you gentlemen seen one of these before?" The doctor held up a condom. His tone held a no-nonsense edge to it. "Hmmm? Well, perhaps you should acquaint yourselves with this helpful little item. Then maybe we won't have to see you in here again." He talked for ten minutes about V.D., rattled off a list of do's and don'ts and handed out several pamphlets. "Any questions? No? Okay, make a follow-up appointment on your way out."

Scott waited for the others to file out of the room before him. He wanted to tell the doctor that he was a Christian, but something held him back. *How can I tell him I'm a Christian? Here I am being treated for V.D. What a great witness that would be.* Scott folded the pamphlets in half and buried them in the back pocket of his jeans. He dug his hands deep in his front pockets and floundered out the door.

Back at home that evening, Scott stood at the kitchen counter, forcing down his fifth glass of water. His long-sleeved shirt concealed the red spot on his arm where blood had been drawn. Sitcom dialogue and canned laughter reverberated from the next room where Gail and Chuck watched television. Through green beads hanging over the kitchen window, he looked out at a street light glowing yellow in the darkness. Later that evening, he wrote in his journal:

I've never felt so alone in my life. I couldn't go to any of my friends for help. How could I tell them I'd gone to a gay bath and now have V.D.? As much as I need comfort and understanding, I couldn't turn to any of my friends. I want desperately to tell my parents, but that would be cruel. That would only hurt them—deeply—and I couldn't do that.

The next two months seemed to plod along. Scott filled his days with activities and detours that occupied his time in an attempt to contain his thoughts. He escaped to the Harlequin theater to watch old movies two or three times a week. Soap operas were a midday ritual. He spent hours on his knees praying for deliverance from temptation. One last trip to the Public Health Clinic cleared Scott of any disease. He pulled stacks of old comic books from his bookshelf and read them for hours. He took Sparkle for long walks around the neighborhood.

He caught the classics *The Pirate* and *Easter Parade* at a local college film festival; he scavenged library archives to find old movie reviews. Life cruised by without incident, except for the time in church when a man told Scott he thought he saw him at the Public Health Clinic. Scott said he'd never been there, that it must have been someone else, and the crisis passed as quickly as it arose. In the midst of the busy months, Scott found time to write in his journal:

The temptations I'm experiencing are incredibly strong. It's so hard to keep myself from doing wrong. I haven't done anything horribly wrong as far as deeds go—not since that night two months ago at the Club 2000—but my thoughts are so awful. I'm afraid of what I might do, yet I can barely control myself.

One Friday afternoon a week later, the battle was over. Scott walked to his car with his school books clutched at his side. The March sun played hide and seek behind billowy clouds, occasionally breaking through to brighten the sky. Scott shifted his books from one hand to the other and waved to a friend driving out of the school parking lot. In the distance he heard the growing din of students leaving the building.

He pulled his car onto the southbound Santa Ana freeway and turned up the radio. His fingers tapped on the steering wheel to the music beat. He weaved through the late afternoon traffic and passed off-ramp after off-ramp. Glancing at himself in the rear-view mirror, he brushed back windblown hair through his fingers. A smile played on his lips as a rock-and-roll beat pulsated from the radio.

He left the freeway, turned onto a side street, turned right at the first light, went straight about a mile, and took a quick left at the liquor store. He slowed the car to a crawl and scanned the street for a parking place. A half block further, he parked behind a white BMW, stepped out of the car, and stopped to peer up at the imposing mauve building rising before him.

SEVEN

Torn Between Two Worlds

A mber leaves blanketed the tiny lawn fronting the Camerons' brick and stucco home. Above the brittle fallen
foliage arched silhouettes of bare trees, and above that
stretched a landscape of winter sky. Mountains of soggy purple
clouds gathered in the west, and where the clouds passed
between earth and the setting sun, they donned brilliant rims
of nothing less than eighteen-karat gold. Where the sun hid from
view, white rays spilled from the valleys between the darkening
billows. It was the kind of sky that drew the practiced eye of
photographers and artists, and the admiration of any who cared
to look.

It was Christmas, halfway into Scott's third year at college
Scott might have stopped to admire the twilight heavens, but
he was pressed for time as he waded blindly through the fallen
leaves, his arms laden with a mountain of shopping bags and
boxes that obscured his sight. He aimed toward the front steps
praying that he could make it all the way to his bedroom without
crossing paths with anyone.

He had just stumbled up the first step, under the eaves of the
porch overhang, when the multi-colored Christmas lights strung
along the rain gutter burst into brilliance. He realized his mother
was just inside the front door, her hand probably still on the
electrical cord she had just connected to the outlet. Then he

shrugged and smiled, nursing an immense new appreciation for the skill his parents had shown in concealing Christmas and birthday secrets throughout his childhood years.

He cracked open the front door. "Mom! Anybody! Close your eyes! Christmas presents coming through!"

He heard his mother holler an "Okay!" from the kitchen. He peered into the living room. Tammy, who had been trimming the artificial Douglas fir, waited with her back to the door and her hands over her eyes. Scott, still balancing unwrapped gifts, made a mad dash for the hallway.

Ah, well, who could say? Maybe by this time next year he'd be in his own apartment. Secrets would be a whole lot easier to keep once he was on his own.

Scott emerged from his room a few minutes later. "Tammy. Seen the Scotch tape?"

"Did you look in the kitchen drawer?"

"No."

"Well, that's where it always is." Tammy rolled her eyes with impatience that was, for the most part, mock. Scott walked past his mom, giving her a brief peck on her cheek as he did. He found the tape in the drawer and started toward his room. As he passed Tammy, she tossed a plastic Christmas ornament at his leg to get his attention.

"Scott, Mitch'll be by any minute. We're gonna watch a movie and bake Christmas cookies."

"You want me to stay out of your way?"

"No-oo!" Tammy crooned. "I was *trying* to say you might get some cookies tonight—if you're nice."

"What an offer!" Scott laughed. "But I'm meeting the guys in my discipleship group. It's the last time we'll get together for a couple of weeks. We canceled next week's meeting 'cause it's so close to Christmas."

Gail, who had just settled in at the kitchen table with the address book and the last of the Christmas cards, looked up at her son. "Well, maybe Mitch'll still be here when you get back."

Scott nodded. "That'd be nice."

Scott smiled to himself, realizing that a few months ago he

couldn't have said that—honestly, at least. Scott was growing to appreciate Mitch Hadley, but it hadn't begun that way.

Right from the start, Tammy's new boyfriend had captured the hearts of the entire family, striking up a rapport with Gail and winning the staunch loyalty of Tammy. Scott could handle *that* part.

What he hadn't handled well was the easy relationship the newcomer enjoyed with Scott's father. Somehow Mitch could talk football with Chuck with a passion that even Scott, the master feigner, couldn't fake. And it wasn't just football. Mitch Hadley, with a wrestler's build and a love for the outdoors, knew the lingo for all the sports, tools, and typically "male" activities that Chuck loved and Scott didn't.

Mitch Hadley was, quite simply, the salt in a secret wound that Scott had quietly nursed for an entire lifetime.

Chuck would have given his life for his son, and Scott knew that. But lurking somewhere in Scott's heart was the sinking feeling that he had never quite met his dad's expectations of a son. Scott's parents had prayed for four years for their firstborn. Sometimes Scott felt it had taken another twenty-one years for Chuck to get the kind of father-son relationship he'd always wanted, and it had arrived with Mitch.

Then five months ago, after a mere month of dating, Mitch and Tammy got engaged. Suddenly Scott's resentment wasn't a temporary discomfort. It looked like Mitch would be around for the long haul.

That was it in a nutshell. Scott felt displaced by Mitch Hadley.

Not that anyone had ever known.

In the past eleven months, Scott had hidden those feelings well, along with a bevy of darker secrets.

Scott was the second to arrive at Joel's house, where five young Christian men—including Tony Lozano, Scott's friend with UPS— had been meeting weekly to read the Bible, pray, and encourage one another. Scott was quick to choose a chair next to Joel's.

Ever since the group formed four months ago—and in light of the falling out with Kirk Graham last Christmas—Scott's growing friendship with Joel Schmidt had been the bright spot in Scott's life.

"Any news from Grace?" Scott asked as he set his Bible next to Joel's on the carpet.

Joel shook his head and frowned. "Not yet. I keep telling myself they haven't had time to process the application yet."

"Well, if you're gonna start classes this spring, they'd better hurry."

Joel nodded. A serious thinker with a great love for Scripture, Joel dreamed of becoming a missionary. The men in the discipleship group had prayed often about his application to a one-year missions program.

Scott smiled to himself. He had another secret, only this one brought him nothing but joy. For the past several months, Scott had set aside every dime he had received in tips from the restaurant. It didn't sound like much, but already his little stash of dimes—stockpiled in a large jar sitting on his desk—had grown to nearly a hundred dollars. One year from now, when Joel was ready for the mission field, Scott was going to present him with the fund. It was Scott's way of playing a small role in the life of a friend.

Sometimes, when Scott was with Joel, he thought of the special friendship that the young King David had shared with Saul's son Jonathan. The two young men had been brothers as much as friends. They had shared struggles and triumphs. There had been camaraderie, spiritual unity, and godly love.

Just last night, Scott had written in his journal:

I want to be Joel's Jonathan.

There it was again. That hunger for a special friendship.

Suddenly Joel turned to Scott. "And what about you?"

"Me?" Scott startled. "I guess I was drifting. Me what?"

"What's going on in *your* life?" Joel asked sincerely. "I'm always burdening you with my stuff. The application. Stuff at work. I feel like I never give you a chance to tell me what's going on with you."

"Thanks for asking, but everything's going pretty well."

Joel pursued the matter. "C'mon Scott, we've all got struggles, challenges. . . . You're always there for me. I want to be there for you, too."

Scott bit his lip. "Well, there is one thing."

"Yeah?"

"Well, if you think about it this week, you might want to pray for me about something."

"Sure, Scott."

"I'm considering a big change in my life. I haven't told anyone yet, because it's still not clear in my head."

"Oh?"

"I'm thinking about switching from journalism. I like to write, but I don't think I could make a living at it. There's this program at my school for respiratory therapists. You know, being responsible for patients' respiratory care in hospitals and stuff. It's a two-year program and I could get a job at one of the facilities in the area."

"Big change from writing, Scott."

Scott shrugged. "I know. But it's good money. And very little risk. In two years I could be out of school, earning a good living, on my own. I can still write on the side—just without the struggle of trying to pay the rent by doing it. Life's hard enough, you know? Who needs more struggle?"

Joel nodded. "When do you have to make up your mind?"

"I've got a couple of months, I think."

"Well, I'll be praying. Just keep me posted on any new developments."

By that time Tony and the others had arrived. The five friends exchanged greetings, and then a college senior named Bill began the evening with prayer.

Two days later, Scott parked his car outside Denny's Coffee Shop. A few minutes later he slid into a booth across a table from Kirk

Graham, home for Christmas after his fifth semester of college.

Kirk, sitting in front of an icy glass of Pepsi, slapped his old friend a high-five. "Saw you drive up, Scott! Looking goo-oood! When'd you get the new wheels?"

"You mean the Mustang? I thought you'd seen it."

"Nope. When I left California last summer, you were still in the Mechanized Monster."

Scott laughed. "You mean the Maverick?"

"One and the same."

"I guess some things have changed, Kirk."

"So tell me what else is going on. I heard Tammy's got a new boyfriend. Serious?"

"I guess so. They're engaged. The wedding's in a couple of months. In March."

"Whoa! Fast work! Do you like him?"

Scott shrugged. "He's nice."

"That's good. How's school?"

"Good."

"That's good."

A buxom waitress interrupted the small talk to take their order. As Kirk snatched a quick look at the menu, Scott studied his friend.

Scott considered Kirk one of his closest friends, yet they had never managed to recapture the closeness they had experienced two summers ago. Last Christmas hadn't helped, when Scott had felt overlooked in the hustle and bustle of Kirk's homecoming from college. And then there had been that night last January, eleven months ago, when Scott's worst nightmare and most perverted fascination had turned into reality at the Club 2000 in downtown Anaheim.

Scott knew he alone was responsible for the decision that had forever altered the fabric and texture of his life. Yet there was a part of him — a small part — that wanted to place the blame on Kirk Graham, maybe even Paul Reardon. Perhaps if he hadn't felt so rejected by them, he wouldn't have given in to the kind of temptations he'd been battling a long, long time.

Now, nearly a year later, he sat across the table from Kirk

and ordered an iced tea and a cheeseburger as calmly as if the past months hadn't been reflections of hell itself, as if he hadn't felt trapped in a *Twilight Zone* episode more surreal and twisted than any that had ever aired on television.

Despite the happy, busy image he projected to his parents and to Tammy, Scott had been treated for venereal disease five times in the past ten months.

Despite his involvement in church and the kinship he felt with the guys in his discipleship group, Scott found himself drawn repeatedly to the dark pain and pleasures behind the doors of the Club 2000.

But more than his lifestyle had been severed into mutually exclusive worlds. His very soul had been sundered as well, and Scott was having a hard time living with the chasm.

His journal entries over the past year had reflected the deep rift that he worked so hard to hide:

I feel so torn and confused—torn between two very different lives. I want to live for Christ, so why can't I abandon my past completely? Why do I keep having setbacks?

I always leave that place feeling so sick inside. I don't even enjoy myself while I'm there, because I know it's so wrong—and then I feel like a tramp when I go home.

I've got to get my head together; I've got to shake myself loose from this trap while there's still time. (And there is time, isn't there?) But how? How do I change? I've made recommitments before, but I haven't made any of them stick. I can try again, and that's what I'll do. . . but how do I make the changes work and last?

I'm so afraid of death. I don't want to die; not while I'm like this. The future seems to bleak, but . . . God knows the future, doesn't He? And God still changes lives, doesn't He? Well . . . I won't give up hope yet . . . no, not yet. Besides, my future is spotless. Maybe I can keep it like that.

I wish I could confide in someone, but I can't . . . and I don't think I ever could. I guess this is one instance when the Lord's grace will really have to be sufficient for me.

At another point he wrote:

When will it stop? Can it stop? Have I got to the point where there's no turning back and I'm just going to ruin myself till I die?

I need help, but I can't talk to anybody about it. And I'm proving to myself that I can't bring about any results myself. So what can be done?

One night, having just woken himself up to take a tetracycline pill to combat yet another bout of V.D., Scott, sick and lonely in a house wrapped in sleep, penned the following:

It isn't just the fear of V.D.; that could be overcome, I guess. But I know that a gay lifestyle—not to mention promiscuous sex—is wrong; God said so. I want to please the Lord. . . . I want my life to honor Him, and I want to spend all of my time serving Him. How could I have gotten so far involved in this? I know that sex was never the major issue. I think that I needed attention—I wanted to be noticed. So I went looking. . . in the wrong places.

I found attention, all right. But at what a price!

My Christian friends, my family, could never understand how I feel. I would never expect them to condone my actions; even I can't do that. But I can understand why I did what I did; I wish they could understand, too.

I'll never tell them, though, and unless they read this (should I die someday) they'll never find out.

It's hard to keep this all to myself—I want to talk with somebody about my problems so badly! But some things just aren't meant to be shared; they have to remain personal. And this is my secret in life: my past, and the lifestyle I continue to battle.

I hope it's a secret that I take with me to my grave.

These thoughts and others swirled in Scott's head as he squeezed lemon into his tea and swapped college updates with Kirk.

The friends talked about Karla, a girl back in Indiana with whom Kirk was pretty serious, and how Kirk wanted Scott in the wedding . . . if Kirk and Karla ever got that far. They talked about test scores and team scores and the number of pretty girls on the cheerleading squads at each of their colleges. They talked about the old days back in high school and what had happened to all the old teachers they had liked the least.

And all the while, Scott wanted to blurt the truth. He wanted Kirk to know the chilling truth—that since last Christmas, Scott had had sexual encounters with more men than he could possibly remember.

But Scott, listening politely to Kirk's tale of some college prank, merely reached across the table for a packet of sugar for his tea, his lips pressed into a hard, thin smile.

Four months later, on a crisp Saturday afternoon in April, Scott and Chuck were in the driveway, hunkered over the engine in Scott's car. Suddenly a latch clicked and the kitchen window slid open. Gail spoke through the curtain of green beads and through the screen.

"Scott, honey, telephone. It's Melanie!"

Scott hesitated, a spark-plug in hand.

Chuck tossed him a towel for his grease-stained hands. "Go ahead, son. I'll keep working."

Scott handed over the plug and bounded inside. He picked up the phone in the hall and carried it into his room.

"Melanie! What a surprise! How've you been?"

"Long time no hear, Cameron. And I've been fine. Really fine. I'm calling with some good news!"

"I'm sitting down."

"I'm engaged!" announced the voice on the phone.

"Geez, Mel. That's *great* news. Don't tell me it's that thirty-year-old man from your church . . . the one in your note."

Melanie laughed. "Gawd, Cameron. What a memory. Was I such a nerf all through high school . . . or was it just that one incident in our senior year?"

"Nerf? Nah, I remember a good friend with a hyena's laugh and a spread of freckles that wouldn't quit."

"So how about you?" Melanie asked. "Last time we talked you were at Western, but I think I ran into someone who said you were in a nursing program somewhere."

"Respiratory therapist, actually, at City College. And I'm changing jobs, too. I'm looking for something part time in the medical field. It's tragic, but at some point in the coming months I'll actually be leaving my job at Polly's Restaurant," Scott added melodramatically.

"After, what . . . two years now?" Melanie estimated.

"About that long. But at least there's another Cameron to carry on the legacy. I got Tammy a job there. She just started working. Oh yeah, I forgot to tell you. She's married now."

"Married! Little Tammy? When? To who?"

"Last month and Mitch Hadley. I don't think you know him."

"Are they happy?" Melanie gushed. "I'll bet it was a beautiful wedding."

"It was. My grandmother made her dress. You should have seen it."

"It's an epidemic, Scott! I heard about Kirk Graham!"

"Well, he's not engaged yet, although he's close. But did you hear about Tony and Caroline?" Scott added.

"No, tell me."

Scott grinned even though Melanie couldn't see him. "The old geezer finally went and proposed. He saved up from his job at the parcel service, bought a nice ring and everything. He's in my discipleship group, so we all knew it was coming. I think he's the first of my really close buddies to bite the dust."

"What a glorious description of matrimony," Melanie said, tongue-in-cheek. "And any news from *your* heartland, Scott? Did you ever find the pot of gold at the end of your rainbow?"

"That's right." Scott remembered. "You wrote something like that in my yearbook, didn't you?"

"Well?"

"Well, let's just say I'm still looking," Scott said vaguely.

"Nothing wrong with that, Scott," Melanie chattered. "You'll know it when it's right."

"I hope so, Melanie."

On Sunday afternoon Scott was on the freeway, heading toward the Club 2000 when the temperature needle on the dash began to creep right. Scott chewed his lip, wondering if he should pull over

Suddenly steam began billowing from beneath the hood. With a small curse, Scott aimed the car at the first off-ramp. The Mustang limped through one light and finally died in the parking lot of a convenience food store.

Scott, sweating, found a pay phone and dialed home. *Why didn't I ever join AAA,* he wondered angrily. As the phone rang, Scott tried desperately to think of some reason for being where he was; a reason he could tell his parents.

The phone clicked. Chuck's voice filled the line. "Cameron residence."

"Dad? Dad, it's me. The . . . the car broke down. I think it needs water or something. It's smoking everywhere."

"Where are you, Scotty?"

Scott squinted beyond the dirty glass of the phone booth and gave his father cross streets.

"Way out there? I thought you were heading into school, son."

"Yeah, well, I was, Dad. But . . . well, I'll explain when you get here. Someone's waiting to use the phone."

Scott hung up and turned to face a parking lot deserted except for his steaming car.

When Chuck arrived with the water can, Scott was ready with a story about being on his way to visit Tammy, who was working the afternoon shift at Polly's Restaurant. The restaurant wasn't too far from this neighborhood, and gave Scott the alibi he needed. By that time, the Mustang had cooled considerably, and the two men were able to get it on the road toward home.

Back home, Scott parked the Mustang and started to follow his dad into the house. But before they left the front yard, Chuck dangled his car keys at Scott. "Don't worry about the Mustang, Scotty. I'll see what the problem is. You go on and get your things done. I know you were planning on going to church tonight. I don't think your mom or I need the car."

Scott hesitated, his stomach twisted into knots over the glaring lie he'd just told his father. He felt sick—physically sick . . . the way he deceived his parents.

And then he took the keys and drove straight for the Club 2000.

By six o'clock that evening, Scott was in church.

Joel found him in the last row and joined him there. A few minutes after the hymns started, Tony and Caroline slipped into the aisle next to Joel, leaning across their friend to wave at Scott.

Scott gave a startlingly good imitation of a smile and then returned his stare toward the pulpit. If the eyes are truly the window to the soul, he hoped no one had seen too much in his.

Halfway through the service, Scott found himself sneaking side glances toward Tony and Caroline. He couldn't see their faces, hidden on the other side of Joel. But he could see that they were holding hands tenderly. And he could see the flash of the B-grade diamond on Caroline's hand.

He thought of Melanie's engagement.

He thought of Tammy and Mitch, glowing on their wedding day.

He thought about Kirk and his sweetheart in the Midwest.

And he thought about the probability that he would never experience that kind of love.

At that final thought, dark waves of grief swelled up and crashed about his head until he felt himself sinking in the swirling black water . . . choking . . . gasping . . . drowning.

On Wednesday night, Scott pulled his Mustang in front of Joel's house. There were no other cars at the curb as Scott climbed from his car and locked the door behind him.

Joel had made a special phone call last night, asking Scott to come early to discipleship. Scott was more than a little curious to see what Joel had on his mind.

Joel broached the subject shortly after grabbing two bottles of Dr. Pepper from his parents' fridge and handing one to Scott, who was sitting in an overstuffed tweed chair by the fireplace.

Joel sat on the edge of a coffee table, facing Scott, his elbows on his knees and his soda between his hands. "Scott, we gotta talk. There's something eating away at you. I just know it. And I'm concerned."

Scott fidgeted in the big tweed chair. "Oh?"

"Yeah. I've sensed it for a while, but Sunday night at church it was pretty obvious."

Scott felt his face redden as the mention of Sunday brought unwanted memories of the overheated Mustang, his deception of his trusting father . . . and the Club 2000.

Joel continued. "Look, my friend. We've shared a lot in discipleship. And I feel like we've grown close . . . like brothers even. Sure, I feel close to the other guys, but you're someone I can really confide in. But it's got to be a two-way street."

The bastard thoughts came thickly now; thoughts and memories that Scott didn't want and he prayed weren't reflected on his face. Joel wanted a two-way street . . . but he had no idea what kind of secrets Scott had to offer. Scott found himself thinking of the familiar rush he felt each time a stranger caught his eye and the two men followed each other to any place in the Club's vast chasms that offered a little comfort and any privacy at all. The Club was filled with dimly lit cubicles and smokey rooms where nameless bodies, sweaty with lust, entwined for a few moments of . . . what? Escape? Passion? Sin? Sex? Excitement? A sense of belonging to a brotherhood of sorts? Membership in a covenant of hurting men bound by their mutual misuse of one another?

There were a lot of things available at the Club 2000.

But love wasn't one of them.

Scott looked into Joel's eyes, intense with a godly concern. Now *this* was love. Agape love. Something pure and holy. Something Scott valued more . . . well, almost more . . . than whatever it was he got from his other life.

Joel pursued the matter. "So do you want to talk about it?"

Scott brushed aside the offer. "Joel, you have no idea what your concern means to me. It's . . . it's priceless. And, yes, there are some things I'm . . . struggling with. But I'm not ready to talk about it. Not yet. Not until I get some things in my life under control."

Joel sighed. "Scott, you don't have to impress me with holiness or godliness to be my friend. Look, we're both gonna fall at times. But if we're accountable to each other, we can lift each other back up."

"Sounds good, Joel, but . . ." Scott trailed off miserably.

"That's the way God created it to be, Scott. That's one of the ways He ministers to us—through our fellowship with each other."

"Yeah, I read something about that in last month's *Campus Life* magazine," Scott admitted. "There was this article on friendship. It said we need to learn transparency—how to let our closest friends see what's in our hearts."

"Exactly!" Joel beamed until Scott's next words cut him off at the knees.

"But not now, Joel," Scott said tersely, desperately. "I can't tell you, yet. I just can't."

Driving home several hours later after the discipleship meeting ended, Scott mulled over thoughts that would later find their way into his journal:

I'm so afraid to let Joel see inside me, because I'm afraid he wouldn't like me if he saw my weakness . . . my vulnerability. But I am weak right now, and I am vulnerable—it all goes with the package.

The thing is, Joel seems to want to be a friend to this package—the entire package—and it means the world to me. I know that I would stand by him through thick and thin—so why don't I trust him to do the same? You can't really love someone without trusting him, so . . . I must develop trust.

Yet I feel so unlovable. I need help right now. I'm more than

*willing to give help to Joel or anyone else who needs it from
me . . . but I'm just not ready to accept it yet. I keep thinking
that I have to get my act together before I try to offer friendship,
rather than during. It's confusing.*

I can't help but wonder, though. . . .

*What if, by making sure I'm completely together before I
begin to open up to my friends, I'm robbing them of the opportunity to help and minister?*

*What if I never get my entire life where I want it . . . or what
if I spend years in the process? Do I keep my friends at arms'
distance that entire time?*

*No, I think not. There must be a happy medium some-
where. . . . I just have to find it.*

Several weeks later, Scott gave Joel the jar of dimes. It contained nearly three hundred dollars. It was near the end of May,
and Joel still had another six months to go before he would be
ready for the mission field. But Scott was too excited about the
gift to wait any longer.

The two friends were at Joel's house, eating homemade
burritos. After Joel recovered from the shock and thrill of Scott's
sacrifice, the conversation ambled on to other subjects.

Scott couldn't have been happier. The Christian fellowship
he shared with Joel fed a long-time void in Scott's soul. Sometimes the friends shared a movie or grabbed a burger. Sometimes
they just sat and talked . . . about school, about God, about
dreams and goals for their lives.

That night began no differently . . . until something happened that cast a pall over the evening and threatened the entire
relationship.

They were talking about old friendships.

"I had a good friend once," Joel shared. "He's a Christian,
but he's an ex-gay."

Scott tried to appear casually interested. "Yeah?"

"Yeah. I didn't know it for a long time."

Scott cleared his throat. "So what happened?"

"So one day he told me all about his past life and the desires he'd had. He told me everything. I guess he was past it all, by that time, but still. . . ."

"Still what?" Scott asked.

Joel shrugged. "Oh, I don't know. The friendship was never the same after that. There was kind of like this . . . this wall between us. I'm not sure if he built it or if I did. But I found myself always wondering if he was having those . . . those kinds of feelings about me. It was a really scary thought. And I guess I just couldn't deal with that."

"Are you guys still friends?" Scott asked in a small voice

Joel shook his head.

And a little part of Scott died inside.

Summer came and went. Scott, still active in his discipleship group, took on additional responsibilities with the college group at church, writing skits and plays and helping to produce them with Tony and other friends. As fall drew near, he prepared for his second semester in the respiratory therapy program and began seriously pursuing a part-time job in the medical field. In September, he applied for a position as a respiratory therapist at St. Luke's, a local hospital.

And for a while—for a few short months—the battle between his worlds seemed to subside.

He occasionally slipped . . . occasionally found himself in the arms or bed of a stranger who, like Scott, sought a balm for hidden voids in a few heated moments of a sexual expression that was both twisted and illicit.

But for surprisingly long periods of time, even weeks and months at a time, Scott managed to be strong, drawing strength from his Christian friends and his relationship with God.

In October, his journal reflected these thoughts:

I know that I'm a Christian. . . . I've never doubted that. In spite of everything, I do love the Lord. I know it sounds impossible to have a relationship with God and still be involved in something this grotesque. . . . Yet God is faithful, and a lot of progress has been made. I don't blow it nearly as often as I used to. Sometimes, though, I go on a binge, when I feel really down on myself, and I turn to the wrong people for comfort.

So many setbacks. I'm so weak! But God is strong. The important thing is that maybe I'm seeing the light at the end of the tunnel. When I'm hearing the Word preached, and singing God's praises, and surrounded by Christians—even the cold ones—the other lifestyle seems so awful and empty!

I've come to the conclusion that I'm not really gay.

It's sad that I've made such compromises . . . that I gave up so much of myself and did so many wrong things, just because I felt so lonely and insecure. There must have been another alternative that I missed somehow.

It's hard, because I've never been able to talk to anybody about any of this. I couldn't tell a friend, or family, or my pastor, because I feared their reactions, and I didn't want to put such a heavy burden on anyone like that. I can't afford counseling by a trained professional, and I don't know what good it would do anyway. Any therapy that I've undergone in the last few months has been straight from God and myself . . . mostly from myself, I guess, because I'm usually too stubborn to listen to God.

How I wish I could change the past . . . undo the things I've done. But it doesn't work that way. All I've got now is the future

The future. What a scary thought.

Oh God . . . have mercy on me, a sinner.

On November 12, one day before his twenty-third birthday Scott found himself at the mall with an acquaintance. The two men were walking into J. C. Penney's department store when someone called Scott's name.

It was a girl from Scott's college Sunday school class. Her name was Sandi. Scott couldn't remember her last name.

Scott, his heart slamming inside his chest, slowed his pace to say hello. Sandi, a slim brunette with a Dorothy Hamill haircut, was petite in every area except her personality. She gushed on and on about doing some early Christmas shopping, about the weather, and about the latest singles' event at church.

She finally asked pointblank whether or not Scott was going to introduce her to his friend. As she spoke, she tossed an admiring eye at the clean-cut, flaxen-haired young man standing next to Scott. She caught the slight upturn of one side of the stranger's mouth and interpreted the small smirk as a smile.

Scott rushed through first-name introductions, then glanced at his watch, and apologized about needing to get on their way. Sandi said she understood and moved on into the flow of traffic exiting the department store.

She made her way into the mall corridor, stopping to price a sequined denim jacket in the window of a fashion outlet. Sandi winced at the price, continuing down the main thoroughfare She ducked into a beauty supply store, browsing the aisles for some time before finally picking out a bright shade of polish and a matching tube of lipstick. She paid for her purchases with a check, then left the store. As she reentered the mall corridor, she shot a subtle glance back toward Penney's, half-hoping to see Scott and his handsome young friend again. She shrugged off a twinge of disappointment and headed for one of the mall exits, toward the section of the parking lot where she'd left her car.

Moments later, Sandi pulled her faded-blue Toyota around to the parking lot exit and waited at a red light, popping gum and swaying to the beat of a Van Halen song on the radio. Suddenly two black-and-whites, lights flashing, swung past her from the avenue into the parking lot. She watched in her rear-view mirror as the cars bounced over speed bumps and hurried toward an entrance near one of the department stores.

The light changed. Sandi slid her foot onto the accelerator. *Looks like I just missed all the action,* she thought as she pulled into traffic. *I wonder what's happening. . . .*

Just then, Sandi spotted a muscled young man on a motorcycle next to her. His hair gusting in the wind, he glanced over and smiled at the brunette who had noticed him. Sandi thought he looked a little like Kurt Russell, except with bigger biceps. She allowed herself a brief flirt, then accelerated enough to leave the motorcycle caught in traffic at the next red light. She didn't, after all, want to encourage anything more than that.

For Sandi, at least, the incident at the mall was forgotten.

Ten minutes later, at a loading dock behind Penney's, aluminum doors barreled open and a small crowd emerged. Two uniformed police officers, each dragging a man in custody, worked their way toward the back-up squad car waiting at the curb.

One of the store managers, a bespeckled man with a pinkish complexion and a nervous twitch, stood on the dock, wringing chubby hands and peering this way and that, hoping no customers were taking note of the fracas. "Queers . . . fags," he mumbled as he twitched.

"Soliciting . . . right in a public place. Lock 'em all up, I say. Just lock 'em up and throw away the key." A plainclothes security guard—the one who had happened upon the offenders in the men's room and had called the police—stood next to his fidgety employer and watched the police do their job.

One of the men, in his late twenties with a smooth face and close-cropped yellow hair, hid the fear in his eyes behind a cocky expression. He resisted the officer's grip and, as a result, found himself hurtled quite forcefully into the back seat of the car.

The other young man went willingly, moving as if in a state of shock, complying with the officer's orders. He received kinder treatment, but not much kinder. As the car door slammed beside him, he stared straight ahead, through the bullet-proof shield separating him from the blue-uniformed driver. Tears stung his eyes. Scott clenched his jaw and swallowed hard, as if hanging on to his tears would somehow stop the universe from crumbling around him.

EIGHT

Lauren

The night, black and glistening with a midnight dew, enveloped Scott. Not even the porch light, which Gail had left burning, provided an oasis in the darkness that seemed to seep into—and out of—Scott's soul. A manila envelope clutched tightly beneath his arm, Scott huddled at the front door and fumbled with his house key. The key, stuck in the tumblers, refused to turn. Scott jiggled it, then rattled the doorknob violently.

Suddenly he froze, listening with his whole body for the sound of his parents stirring inside. A chorus of crickets mocked him with shrill chirrups that seemed raucous enough to wake the neighborhood. Still he waited, the chill November night icy on his face.

After what felt like an eternity, Scott began to breathe again. He moved and rejiggled the key, quietly this time. The tumblers turned. He slipped inside.

The house was dark, except for the microwave clock that glowed neon green.

It was 1:23 a.m.

Still clutching the envelope, Scott felt his way toward his bedroom, being careful not to bang a shin on the coffee table or run into the floor lamp. In his room, he closed the door gingerly behind him. The latch clicked.

Scott never touched the lights. He welcomed the darkness. He closed his eyes and imagined it absorbing him . . . absorbing a little of the humiliation and grief of the past nine hours. If there had been a light in the room or even an open shutter though which the moonlight might slip—and if there had been a friend there to notice—that friend would have seen tear tracks on a face white with agony. But there was no one to see. And no light left to see by.

Scott sat on the edge of the bed and painstakingly opened the envelope. He held it high above the bed and tipped it, listening to the clink and thump of small things hitting the mattress: His wallet. His watch. A handful of change. A ballpoint. An open roll of Certs. Maybe his comb, but Scott couldn't remember, and he couldn't distinguish the shapes in the dark. They were *his* things, searched and detained and, much later, returned. . . . All done with the maddening nonchalance exhibited by public servants deathly bored with dull and routine jobs. Scott had been finger-printed, photographed, questioned, and finally detained in a holding cell with urine-stained mattresses and the lingering smell of vomit . . . while his uniformed captors complained about the coffee, filed paperwork, and eyed the bosom of one particularly well-endowed clerk named Doris.

It was like an episode of *The Twilight Zone.*

And all the while Scott had been dying inside. Like a dying star, his world had exploded . . . no, imploded . . . and all that was left was a gaping black hole, swallowing up everything in its wake: Purpose. Life. Joy. Dignity.

Gone . . . all gone. Family. Friends. Love. Hope. God.

Yes, even God seemed, at that very moment, smaller than the hungry black hole.

Scott stood up, his hands groping blindly for his desk, and then for the phone. Despite the hour of the night, he punched the buttons by heart and waited, breath held, for the first ring.

A moment later, Scott's tenuous voice trembled from somewhere in the pitch-black room.

"It's me, Scott. Listen, I'm sorry to call so late, but I really needed a friend. I'm, well, I'm in trouble. Serious trouble. . . .

Well, that's the thing. I can't tell you any details. . . . Because, well, I just can't right now. . . . Look, I'll tell you later, but I just needed a friendly voice, you know, some support. . . . Yeah, thanks, that helps." Scott rubbed his eyes, grainy from lack of sleep, with the palm of one hand. "Look, I'll let you go. I'm going to call Kirk in the morning. . . . No, no one else. Just you two."

Scott's birthday, the day after his arrest, passed in a painful blur The kindnesses of his family and friends only twisted the knife of guilt that festered in his heart. The trial was in three weeks. In less than a month, authorities would determine Scott's guilt on charges of disturbing the peace and soliciting sex in a public restroom. In three weeks, Scott's dark secret could hit the light, sending him to jail, humiliating his family, and alienating him from everyone he loved . . . or he could be given a second chance.

A second chance . . . to do what? Return to his dark secret . . . or rebuild his life?

One week before the trial, Scott wrote:

Scott Cameron died two weeks ago. I killed him.

It's too painful to talk about, really . . . but on November 12, something so awful happened that my whole life changed. I know that, from now until I die, I'll view that day as a turning point in my life and think of everything else in relation to before and after that day.

As time goes on, maybe I'll be able to talk about it—but not yet.

I've kept this to myself, telling Joel and Kirk only the minimum—for prayer support, and because I just needed someone to talk to. I go to court on Wednesday, hopefully just to pay a fine. But the outcome could be a lot more disastrous than that.

I've grown a lot in the past two weeks . . . since I died.

I can't believe how dangerously I've been living for the past three years. My God . . . where was my head? I thought I knew the difference between right and wrong, but . . . maybe I didn't, after all.

Now, my eyes see everything so clearly, and I just can't believe that I could have been enslaved for so long.

And that's why my old self had to die. Always before, I've managed to weaken it, or shove it in some corner—but it was always there, waiting for a chance to gain control again. And it always did, too.

I think it's over now, though—the sinning, at any rate. The consequences and repercussions may last for years, but . . . I can take that, as long as there is no more sinning.

Oh, God . . . I'm so sorry I've made such a mess of things. I'm sorry that I shamed You before other men, because I brought shame to myself. I'm sorry if the life I've been leading will cause people pain—and possibly to doubt You.

I'm sorry that I took my reputation for granted—both my public testimony and my deep, personal relationships. I'm sorry that I viewed these relationships as important, yet not important enough to truly guard with all my heart. I'm sorry that I put my friends in a tough position, where they might not want to stay close to me after all.

I'm sorry that I was so blind . . . not seeing the whole truth.

I'm sorry for all the pain . . . not because I'm not deserving of pain, but because I know that the pain has caused me to be so ineffective . . . so unloving. I'm sorry for the scars I have—and could very well carry for a lifetime.

I wish that You were here, Lord Jesus, so I could wash Your feet with my tears and dry them with my hair. How I love You. . . . It's so true that the one who is forgiven much loves much. Through all of this I have learned one thing: I am Your child and part of Your family, and nothing will ever separate me from Your love. In fact, my motivation for changing and doing good is not fear of recrimination, or guilt . . . but out of love. Love for You, love for the handful of people that I hold dearer than my life, and . . . hopefully, someday . . . love for myself.

I'm sure that, if the whole story comes out, there will be many people who look at my life and consider it a tragedy. I hate that, because it isn't a tragedy. When You, God, can touch a life and make it into something beautiful like You have done with mine . . . how can that be anything but victory?

The Bible says that there is much joy in Heaven over the return of one lost sinner . . . and I have come back to You.

Oh, Father . . . I want to get past all the mistakes and make my life count for You.

I just want to be more like You—feeling Your love flow through me, healing all my soul's diseases. I want to be effective, and faithful . . . and pure.

I think about Mary Magdalene a lot—the prostitute that Jesus forgave and loved . . . and changed. I think it's neat to trace her through the Scriptures and see how she became a godly woman, faithful to the end, even when Jesus' own disciples ran away.

Maybe . . . maybe when you've lost your reputation, and you become as nothing in the eyes of men . . . maybe that's when you can finally become useful to God.

I hate myself for what I've done, and I'm not so sure that most of my friends won't hate me, too . . . if and when they find out.

But I know that God loves me, and His love heals so many things.

Oh God . . . it hurts so much. I can't tell You how much. I don't want the others to find out, because I don't think they could handle it. I know that Joel and Tony and Caroline and even Kirk would try to understand, but how could they? Even I don't understand completely.

I'm afraid that they'll completely lose track of who I am, and the fact that I have loved them. There have been so many good qualities in my life, which I've shared with them—but I'm afraid that they'll lose sight of all that, in the shadow of this one thing, which is so bad.

Sigh . . . I know that none of my worrying can accomplish anything.

Maybe this is one of those areas where I should just stop fighting and let God carry me for a while. Maybe, by resting in Him, I'll find perfect peace.

And the strength to endure whatever may come.

Two evenings passed, and Scott found himself at a restaurant, eating dinner with a small band of friends from church. Scott played his role convincingly, coming across as only slightly moody instead of thoroughly devastated.

Halfway through dinner, Joel, who had been sitting at the other end of the table, came around and dragged an empty chair next to Scott. He slid close for privacy.

"I've been praying for you, buddy," Joel said quietly. "Your phone call that night really spooked me. I just wish you'd tell me what happened."

"Joel . . ." Scott shook his head.

"I know, I know. But it's hard trying to support you when I don't even know what the crisis was."

"Was?" Scott snorted. "It's far from over, Joel. Whether I like it or not, you may be getting all the details sooner than you think. There's a . . . I can hardly say the words. There's a *trial* five days from now."

Joel sat stunned for a moment. "A *trial?* Scott . . . what's happening? Tell me what's happening."

Scott winced. "Later. After this blows over. Or maybe when it hits the fan. I don't know. Just wait. Just be patient. And pray, Joel. Please pray for me."

After dinner, the gang decided to take in a movie. Despite Scott's passion for the big screen, he begged off, fired up his Mustang and tore out of the lot.

Soon he was on the freeway, cruising through southbound traffic. Oncoming headlights shone in his eyes and illuminated a face riddled with indecision. Another two off-ramps passed before Scott exited down the third. He pulled over to the side of the road and let the car idle while he took a few minutes to think this through. Street lights chased the darkness from half of his face, while the other half remained encased in shadows. Light and darkness, hope and despair, salvation and damnation, right and wrong, flickered back and forth on Scott's face, between the brightness and the shadows, between Scott's spirit and his flesh.

After several minutes—minutes that held the weight of

hours—Scott hit the accelerator. He whipped a tire-burning U-turn and headed for home.

It was the first time he had ever come this close to the fires of the Club 2000 and made the decision to flee from the heat.

Maybe this was a turning point, after all.

Annie Rankin was a tall brunette with a boyish figure and a heart-shaped face. She had worked at Polly's Restaurant for the past eighteen months and would miss Scott Cameron when he finally took that new job over at the hospital. In her apartment on the east end of town, she set a plate of Oreos on the coffee table and wiped her hands nervously onto the leggings she wore beneath an oversized sweat shirt she'd picked up in Las Vegas. For the ninth time in the past half-hour, she glanced at the digital clock on the bookshelf, sitting next to a photo gallery of her family, her friends, and her roommate, Leann.

At six minutes past eight o'clock, the intercom buzzed. She ran to the door and pushed the button that would unlock the front gate. A moment later there was a knock. Pausing just long enough to take a deep, bracing breath, Annie opened the door to Scott Cameron.

She smiled brightly. "Come in. Hurry, it's cold out there."

"Yeah, turkey weather," Scott said, wiping his shoes on the porch mat before entering. "You sticking around for Thanksgiving? Or are you heading south to see your folks?"

"Here, I'll take your jacket. I'm staying here, with Leann and some friends. It'll be a nice change from all the family soap opera crap that goes with the holidays."

"Hey, wait a minute," Scott grinned. "I like soap operas."

"Sorry, I forgot. So . . . sit down. Want something to drink? Coffee? Tea? Beer?"

Scott's eyes roamed to the coffee table and the plate of cookies. "Oreos? Great. Got any milk?"

"Coming up." Annie headed toward the kitchenette. "I guess that's the best choice with Oreos . . . but if you want I can serve it up in a dirty glass. Won't seem so, well, harmless that way."

Scott smiled. "I can live with harmless."

Annie returned a moment later, and the facade was gone. Scott caught her nervousness long before he noticed the tray of glasses in her hands.

"Annie, what's wrong?"

Annie put the milk on the table. She'd poured something stronger for herself. She took a quick sip of wine before she spoke. "Well, you can probably guess I didn't invite you here just to chat."

"I figured."

"We've been friends for a while now, Scott. Almost two years now. And I like you. I think you're a super guy."

"If this is to say goodbye, Annie, you know I don't leave the restaurant for another couple weeks. . . ."

"No, no. This is something else. Something I wanted to talk about before you left, and I didn't want to do it at work."

"Okay."

"It's that . . . it's just that . . . I know that you know I'm well, gay."

Scott set a half-eaten Oreo on the coffee table. "Oh. *That.*"

"Russell told me he told you," she explained, referring to the busboy who had been fired last month for pilfering cans of food.

"Yeah, yeah . . . he told me," Scott admitted. "I just figured it was your life, and you probably didn't need my interfering."

"Did you know Russell is gay, too?"

Scott, dumbfounded, shook his head in silence.

Annie sighed. "I wondered if you knew. Anyway, he is."

"So why are you telling me all this?" Scott asked, an edge to his voice that surprised even him.

"C'mon, Scott, we're friends. You're leaving, and I just didn't want this big thing between us that we could never talk about. I knew you knew, and I wanted you to *know* I knew you knew I just hoped . . . I just hoped it wouldn't make a difference in our friendship."

"It doesn't change anything," Scott swallowed hard. "We're friends, and your being gay doesn't change that."

"Thanks."

"But. . . ."

"But what?" Annie stared at Scott. He hesitated. "But *what?*"

"I can't lie to you and say I think your lifestyle is great. Because I don't. I think it's wrong, and I'm afraid you're going to find out it isn't what you want. And you're going to get hurt." Scott paused, then plunged ahead. "But even more importantly, I think. . . . Geez, Annie, I hope you don't mind me saying this—I think it's just another obstacle in the way of you ever finding peace with God."

"God?" Annie said sharply. "What does God have to do with it? Just because I'm gay means I can't find God?"

Scott gulped. "Look, I'm not going to preach to you, but God says homosexuality is wrong. And I think He had some pretty good reasons for saying it, too. I just don't want you to get so caught up in things that you don't see the reasons until it's too late. Or worse, get so caught up in the lifestyle that you never see the loving God behind those reasons."

"Scott, nobody's perfect. Everybody has their 'things.'"

"What 'things'?"

Annie sighed impatiently. "Their *things*, Scott. Imperfections. Little secrets. The taboos in our lives. Everyone's got them. So I'm gay. Big deal! The waitress on the next shift is having an affair with the boss. The customer smoking the cigar at table B happens to beat his kids. That one's an alcoholic. This one snorts a line now and then. Frank over there sleeps with anything in a skirt. The teller at the bank binges and purges till her guts ache and her head pounds. The pastor at the church next door skims the offering twice a month. Nobody's a saint, Scott."

"Annie, I'm not saying you've got to be. . . ."

"No one's any better than the next guy, Scott," Annie blurted. "No one. Not even you."

Scott stopped and stared. "What do you mean?"

"God, I'm sorry, Scott. I'm sorry. I meant to bring it up . . . well, gentle-like, not just blurt it out. I'm such a fat mouth."

"What do you mean?" Scott repeated, slowly this time.

"Look. I probably don't have a right to say this, but . . . well, we're friends. And I think we should talk about it."

"Stop stalling."

"Okay, fine. It's just that, before Russell got canned, we used to talk. And Russell and I think . . . well, we think you're gay."

Scott flinched. He tried not to act alarmed, but his face betrayed him as the color drained from his skin. Tense seconds passed. Finally Scott looked at Annie and cleared his throat.

"I won't kid you, Annie. I've struggled in that area. I've struggled a lot. But that's behind me now. I've made a decision to do what I believe is right. For me that means playing it straight."

Annie sat silent, waiting for Scott to continue.

"And as long as I'm being honest," Scott sighed, "I might as well tell you, I'm in some trouble right now. Maybe I shouldn't . . . dang it, Annie, this is hard for me to tell you. A couple weeks ago, a friend and I were at the mall. We went to the restroom, and my friend tried to pick up on this other guy who was in there, you know, just doing his business. It turned out the guy was an undercover security guard with the department store."

Annie clapped one hand over her mouth.

"I know. Real smart, huh? Well, the next thing I know, *I'm* being hauled in for solicitation. I go to trial in two days. I could go to jail—*jail!* Annie, I'm really scared. You're the first one I've told."

"Oh, Scott, I'm sorry! What could happen? At the trial, I mean."

"I don't know. My lawyer says it depends on how strong their case is."

"And *no one* else knows? No one?"

"No one. I mean, two friends know I'm in some kind of trouble with the law, but they have no idea what it is. I can't tell a soul. And please, you don't tell either, okay? You didn't grow up in the church. You don't even go to church. There are some things church people just can't accept. I'm on my own for this one. I've got to get through this by myself. And then. . . ."

"And then?" Annie repeated.

"And then the game's over for me, Annie. I'm going straight. I'm cashing in my chips while I've got something left to play with."

Three days later, in a musty wood-paneled room somewhere in the catacombs of the Norwalk city hall, the trial was over.

The district attorney and judge dropped the original charges, agreed on the "disturbing the peace" charge, and fined Scott $200. They placed him on a year's probation and sent him home, a man with a second chance.

Within a matter of a moment, a heartbeat, a pronouncement, Scott's world had been salvaged. It actually held the bright promise of hope.

I've lived under the shadow of this thing for weeks, and many times I came close to cracking under the strain. But now it's over. I cried all the way home from court and all I could say was, "Thank You, Father," over and over.

I called Joel with the good news. He had been praying for me and was with me every step—even though he didn't know exactly what was going on. I owe him a debt of love.

Maybe we really do need each other. Not as crutches, but maybe like braces. Friends can't do the walking for us, but they can offer support as we go through the painful process of walking.

I think I've learned that I can't conquer problems on my own.

So where do I go from here? Certainly not back to where I was before. I have a second chance, and I'm not going to blow it. I have the freedom to determine how I live.

My old lifestyle is over. Completely over.

The ring of the phone at his elbow startled Scott's thoughts. He capped his pen and reached for the receiver. "Hello?"

"Hi. It's Kirk. What happened? Is everything okay?"

"It's over! I'm cleared as of . . ." Scott peered behind him at the alarm clock on the bed table, "as of forty-nine minutes ago."

"Are you relieved?"

"If you only knew!"

Kirk added wistfully, "I still wish you would've let me go with you. I don't know what could be so terrible that you're hiding."

Scott paused. "Well, to be honest with you, I'd . . . I think we should talk about it another time. Okay?"

"Okay, sure. But you know I'm always willing to listen." Kirk cleared his throat. "Well, so much for the good news." His light tone turned dark, heavy. "Listen, I've got something to tell you. This will be painful, Scott."

"What? What's going on?"

"It's Melanie," Kirk said.

"What? About her wedding? What happened?"

"No, not about that. She was in a car accident."

"God, no. . . ."

"It's serious, Scott. She's . . . she's dead."

The phone line fell silent, but Kirk could sense Scott's torrent of dark emotions despite the distance between them.

When Scott finally spoke, his voice was hoarse. "When?"

"Last night."

"The funeral?"

"Friday morning. Forest Lawn. The one in Cypress."

"I can't talk about it right now, Kirk," Scott said, forcing the words past the aching lump in his throat. He squeezed his eyes shut against the tears and felt the room spin momentarily.

"I understand. I guess I'll see you on Friday."

"I guess you will."

Friday dawned with a vengeance. The late November skies, ripped apart, drove sheets of rain relentlessly on the little white chapel as cars of mourners pulled to a stop and clusters of darkly clad figures scurried indoors. Inside the tiny sanctuary, nearly every seat was filled as friends and family gathered to nurse their throbbing grief and seek a little comfort from the storm of pain. Secluded behind a curtain with Melanie's parents and sisters, Melanie's husband-to-be sat clutching the wedding ring that would have adorned Melanie's hand in less than one month.

Scott spotted several friends he hadn't seen since high school. Scanning the sea of solemn faces, Scott noticed the towhead of Paul Reardon. The face brought back memories, but few feelings, thank God.

By the time the little service drew to a close, pinpoints of sunlight had broken through the rain-whipped skies. Scott let himself be carried by the stream of mourners out of the heated sanctuary and into the cold. Moments later, the gathering of family and friends had regrouped on a grassy slope at the site of Melanie's grave. Scott stood beside Tony and Caroline. Caroline's heels sunk deep into the rain-soaked hill. From where they were plastered on the ground, wet leaves stained with the colors of fall lifted and blew each time the wind gusted.

Scott's mind swirled with thoughts of life and death and eternity and evil. He found himself asking the age-old question: why good, loving people had to die while others racked up the years with fruitless, deceptive, and even dangerous lives.

Somehow Christmas passed. On Christmas day, Scott's grandmother gave Scott and Tammy each a check for $200–the exact amount Scott needed to pay his court fine. Tammy and Mitch were thrilled, announcing that the money would buy the dryer they desperately needed for their rented home. Scott just gave his grandmother a big kiss, saying nothing more than that the money would go for a good cause.

New Year's Day came and went, kicking off the year 1981 Scott prayed that it signaled a new beginning for him, as well.

In the third week in February, Scott parked his Mustang in the employee parking lot of St. Luke's Hospital. It was his first day on the job as a respiratory therapist. He found the Personnel Office and spent his first hour filling out his W-4 and other paperwork. Later, walking down sterile white halls dotted with institutional paintings of mountain ranges and seascapes, Scott bit back a smile. This was his first *real* job.

But what timing. The past couple of months had been jam packed with the kind of events that send the numbers through the ceiling on one of those stress tests. If Scott remembered correctly, the test consisted of a list of events–happy as well as tragic–with each event assigned a stress point value. Even Christmas was on the list.

Scott reviewed his life lately. Some of the things he'd experienced recently were top stress producers according to the test. Other things weren't listed on the test . . . but should have been ranked at the very top. In the past three months Scott had:

Buried a friend. . . .

Quit his job. . . .

Started a new job. . . .

Survived finals week at school. . . .

Been arrested and tried for a humiliating crime. . . .

Been confronted, the first time ever, about a life-long secret. . . .

Given up the gay lifestyle. . . .

And, yes, even celebrated Christmas.

Scott nodded to passing nurses and orderlies as he strode toward the station to report in. His own crisp blue hospital shirt and I.D. badge gave him a feeling of belonging. Yet his inner thoughts and feelings reflected anything but confidence. There was a knot in the pit of his stomach that felt like a cannonball.

Suddenly he passed a woman weeping outside a patient's room, and he was struck with, at once, a painful memory and a new resolution: *Maybe I can help someone like Melanie by working here. Maybe I can bring encouragement to hurting people.*

He rounded the corner on the two-north floor and walked toward the nurses' station. Two women sat there chatting, drinking coffee, before their shift began. One of the women faced Scott; the other had her back turned toward him.

"Hi, I'm Scott Cameron," he interjected in a lull in the conversation. "This is my first day on the job. Am I supposed to check in here?"

"You'll want to see Nick," responded the first woman, huskily built with a voice to match. "He should be back in a minute. He'll tell you everything you need to know."

Suddenly the second woman, her back to Scott, turned to face him. "Scott Cameron! It's been a long time. Do you remember me?"

The face was familiar. Scott ran a quick search of his memory. All of a sudden he smiled, remembering a girl from his high school years. "Lauren Maden!"

"Welcome to St. Luke's." A strawberry blonde with a broad, warm smile, Lauren had flawless skin the color of a new peach and sea-blue eyes that twinkled when she spoke.

"Thanks," Scott paused. "So do you both work on this floor?"

Lauren nodded. "Yeah, I'm an RN, and Glenda here is our receptionist. I've been here about a year and a half. It's a nice place to. . . ."

"There goes Nick," Glenda interrupted, pointing down the hall toward the lunch room where a hulking man with the build of an athlete was disappearing around a corner. "Hurry. You don't want him to think you were late on your first day."

"The second day maybe, but not the first," Lauren teased.

"Well, thanks, and nice to meet you both," Scott said over his shoulder, striking off behind Nick.

Glenda drew her coffee cup to her mouth, sipped, then immediately resumed the gossip that Scott had delayed with his questions. As Glenda gloried in the details of the newest doctor's hostile divorce, Lauren fell pensive, her thoughts still on the broad-shouldered young man with the locks of auburn hair.

On Saturday morning, Scott sat at a table in the Park Pantry restaurant, stirring sugar into a mug of steaming tea and waiting for Tony to arrive. The cafe hosted a few families, a handful of couples, and several aged men sitting alone, soaking in newspapers and hot, strong coffee.

"You ready to order now, honey?" asked a waitress wearing an outdated brown and white uniform, a small hat perched atop her head.

"I'm waiting for a friend. He'll be here in a minute."

Scott watched the waitress bustle away, and his eyes returned to his teacup. Both hands encased the mug as his stare penetrated the murky tea water.

Scott had made a decision.

Now all he had to do was carry it through.

The time was ripe. Past ripe. It was something Scott should have done a long time ago, in fact. Not that he allowed himself much remorse over his procrastination on this matter . . . if he were going to feel remorse about anything in his past, he had many more potent mistakes to rue.

This is it. I'm going to tell Tony all my struggles. I'm finally going to come clean and tell him the truth. I've carried this load by myself for too long.

Scott's decision had come, in part, because of Annie. Her astute observation had broken a dam of sorts.

The decision had come, in part, because of Scott's close call with the law, and the turning point that the crisis had inspired.

It came, in part, because of Melanie. Melanie and Scott had shared a lot through the years: drill-sergeant teachers, notes in class, church summer camps. They had shared advice, camaraderie, and gossip galore. They had cheered each other on during the lean times; kept each other humble during the fat times as only the closest of friends can do. Yet Melanie had died without ever knowing the real Scott Cameron.

It was an alarming thought.

But not as alarming as the thought that followed it: Did anyone know the real Scott Cameron?

Finally, Scott's decision to talk to Tony had been fueled by an even simpler reason: Scott was beginning to wonder if he, alone, could hold himself accountable to his new resolve of celibacy. Giving up the gay lifestyle wasn't going to be as easy as Scott had hoped, despite his close call with prison three months ago. Even since then, Scott had already . . . well, slipped.

Scott needed help.

I can trust Tony. All the guys in our discipleship group have been real open and vulnerable. And Tony has pursued me as a friend. I need the support of someone like him.

"Am I late or are you early?" Tony's voice broke into Scott's train of thoughts. Scott startled and looked up at him. Tony extended his hand, and Scott grasped it warmly.

Scott gestured. "Have a seat. If you're wondering who's to blame, of course I'll say it's your fault."

Perusing menus, the friends alternated between conversation and breakfast decisions.

"So the new job's okay so far, huh?" Tony asked.

"Yeah, I'm catching on pretty quickly, and everybody seems real nice. Did you decide what you're getting?" Scott asked.

"Blueberry pancakes. Now, tell me more about this Lauren you mentioned on the phone."

"Pancakes?" Scott repeated. "Sounds good to me, too."

Tony persisted. "Scott, so what about this Lauren girl? Her name wasn't familiar from high school . . . but I can always look her up in the ol' yearbook."

"But then again, they make a mean cheese omelette here " Scott added.

Tony groaned and smacked his palm to his forehead. "Sure sure, an omelette. But what about *Lauren?*"

Scott concentrated on his menu. "Or I could have the bacon and egg special."

Tony gave in. "All right, you turkey, I get the hint. You don't want to talk about it."

Scott grinned. "It's not that, Tony. It's just that there's not much to talk about. Sheesh! All I said was that there was this girl from our high school, and that she was nice. And you make a federal case about it. Aren't you overreacting a bit?"

Tony shook his head. "No way! This *is* a federal case! As rarely as you tell me about *any* female interest of yours, this is big time, Scott."

Scott laughed. "Nah, I think you've just got weddings on the brain."

After they ordered, the two talked about Tony's upcoming June marriage to Caroline, about the discipleship group, and about friends at church. When the food arrived ten minutes later, Tony offered to say grace. As Tony launched into a prayer Scott's mind spun back to the journal entry he had written earlier that morning.

*The choice is obvious: I can renounce family, friends, faith,
develop the deviant side of my personality, and live my life
exactly as I want until I die. Or I can rise above all this and start
to be the person I know I should be.*

*But I think I've gone too far—maybe there's no turning back.
Maybe I gave up too much of myself along the way, and there's
nothing left to salvage. Anyway, if I do turn back to what I know
is right, I can't do it alone.*

I need a friend—like Joel or Tony—to help me.

". . . Your blessings. Amen." Tony ended his prayer and
looked up, intercepting Scott's line of vision, which was suddenly
fixed on his friend.

"Tony, there's something I want to talk to you about."

"Sure, what is it?"

"Well, this isn't easy for me, but I trust you. I've been struggling
with some things for quite a while." Scott pried the words out,
slowly, painfully. "I've been struggling for several years, in fact.
This problem has plagued me and torn me down . . . even as
recently as . . . well, as recently as last night. It's really built a
wall between me and God. I keep trying to change myself . . . to
get things together, but I just can't seem to do it."

"What kind of struggles are you talking about, Scott?"

Scott gulped a bite of omelette and took a swig of tea. He
stalled for a moment while his mind raced.

"I'm not sure it's necessary to go into all that," he finally said.
"I'm just struggling, that's all. And I need a brother to lean on."

Tony set his fork on the plate and looked at Scott. "You know
you can lean on me. It would help me, though, to know what
you're dealing with, what we're up against."

For a few tight moments, the two ate in silence, as Tony
waited for a reply.

"Well, for some time . . . for a while anyway," Scott groped
for words, "I've been struggling with feelings—unhealthy feelings . . . destructive."

"Go on."

Scott stared down at his half-eaten cheese omelette. He

wrestled to pull together wild, rampant thoughts and emotions

"Last night, I was reading in James about Rahab. It was so encouraging." He looked up at Tony. The words came soft and faint. "I mean, she was a *prostitute*, but she was still used by God. She certainly wasn't perfect, but God worked through her. If God can do that for her, what about me? I guess . . . I guess I'm not convinced yet that God can forgive and restore me. But I want to believe."

Tony stared at his friend, realizing that it was more than a table that separated them. Something very real and very deep was troubling Scott.

"Well, I'm convinced, Scott. God's in the business of forgiving and restoring. I believe the best about you, and I know God can help you through whatever you're dealing with."

Scott forced a weak smile. He let his gaze fall on his teacup

Tony, my friend, you have no idea what I'm dealing with. The thoughts reverberated within Scott's head. *I'm in a trap. If I ever want to be whole again I need to make some radical changes in my life. I need to rely on God's strength. Yet sometimes I hate church and the people there . . . maybe because I hate the way I have to pretend when I'm there. I'm thinking of leaving the church to get to know Jesus for who He is in relation to me, not to the church. There's a war raging inside of me! I want to be whole again. But how? I can't tell anyone what I'm dealing with. I just can't.*

"Maybe you should share your problem with our discipleship group," Tony suggested hesitantly. He sensed a torrent of emotion in his friend. "We've been together nearly a year now. We've been pretty open with each other. That's what we're there for, to help each other out."

"Thanks. I almost thought I was ready for that, but maybe not. Maybe not quite yet. Besides, I know what I need to do—I just need to do it."

Several months later, during the first weeks of spring, the unthinkable happened.

Scott's discipleship group folded from lack of commitment.

Joel had a seminary class the night the group met, Tony was feeling the pressure of his upcoming wedding, and two other members succumbed to a mixture of busyness and apathy. Just as a carcass gives birth to nests of hungry maggots, for Scott the death of the group spawned anger, hurt, doubt, and resentment — hungry parasites that gnawed fiercely at his soul.

Soon personal doubts waged guerrilla warfare in Scott's mind. Behind even Scott's best intentions lurked dark, unconquerable thoughts. His Bible study and prayer life ebbed and flowed with the inconsistency of his weakening resolve to leave the gay lifestyle once and for all.

As the weeks passed, Scott fought a mounting intolerance for church and impatience with his spiritual growth. Phone calls to church friends seemed to go unanswered. Still, he clung to his decision to forge a new, pure path. But deep inside, Scott knew that his resolve was beginning to melt like a sugar cube in the flame.

On the third of June, Tony and Caroline finally tied the knot. Scott, who had known the bride and groom since high school, wished his friends nothing but the best as they became man and wife. At the reception, Kirk approached Scott with news of his own: he was engaged to Karla, the girl from college he'd been dating for some time now. Over cake and punch, Kirk asked Scott if he would be in the wedding. "You've known me about as long as anyone, Scott," Kirk admitted. "And I can't think of anyone whose friendship I value more than yours." Scott accepted, his eyes misting as he did.

One week later, Tony and Caroline were still honeymooning in Mexico when Scott received a phone call from a Mrs. Roberts with the Red Cross. It appeared that the blood Scott had donated during a recent hospital blood drive was . . . well, unacceptable. Routine screening procedures had unearthed in Scott's blood an antigen for a rare form of hepatitis. Scott was advised to seek medical attention right away.

By the time Scott received the test results from his doctor, they were redundant. Scott had all the symptoms: Extreme fatigue, diarrhea, vomiting. The doctor ordered bed rest for a couple of weeks and kept Scott under observation.

A month into his recovery, Scott found himself at a local restaurant, eating Saturday brunch with Lauren Maden. In the past months, they had become friends, due in part to the time they spent working the night shift together at St. Luke's.

Scott, sampling an apple and cheddar omelette, was remarking to Lauren about his recent bout with hepatitis. "They diagnosed me with hepatitis B, and started to treat me with. . . ."

"Hepatitis B," Lauren interrupted, Scott's words stirring something in her memory. "That's prevalent among gays and drug abusers, right?"

"Well, yeah," Scott admitted. "But that's why the doctor wants to write me up in some medical journal."

"A journal? Really?"

Scott nodded. "Really. You're right—it seems only gay men and IV drug users get this particular strain. But I'm neither, so the doctors were pretty amazed. They weren't quite sure how to treat me."

"You're neither." Lauren—her heart pounding doubletime in her chest—urged Scott for a clarification.

Scott cleared his throat. "I'm neither gay nor am I an IV drug user."

Lauren turned quickly to her hash browns, averting her eyes to hide the hope that sprang there.

Just last week, Lauren and Glenda had discussed Scott Cameron during their coffee break. It had been simply one more in a series of conversations during which Glenda swore that the good looking respiratory therapist was homosexual. But Lauren, as usual, had been slow to accept Glenda's judgment. "He's a Christian," Lauren had justified to her own heart as well as to Glenda. "He can't be gay. . . . Can he?"

Now, sitting across from Scott Cameron, chatting calmly over hash browns and omelettes, Lauren felt a flare of hope and the warmth of a blush creeping up her cheeks.

Scott Cameron wasn't gay!

Several weeks later, on a muggy August evening, a Mustang rumbled down a moonlit street. The windows were down and rock-and-roll preceded the car by half a block. The car pulled abruptly in front of a house illumined with a brightly burning porch light. Scott climbed from the car, slamming the car door behind him with his sneakered foot. Humming to himself, he crossed the lawn, tossing his keys in the air and catching them with an overhand sweep.

Inside the house, Gail and Chuck were watching the late news. They turned toward the front door as it barreled open.

"Nice evening?" Chuck asked.

"Real nice," Scott answered, unzipping his windbreaker and heading toward the kitchen for a Pepsi.

"Were you with Tony and Joel?" asked Gail. "I haven't seen them much lately."

"No, not Tony and Joel," Scott answered from the kitchen. A moment later he reappeared, popping the top of a can as he walked toward his bedroom. "This was another friend. . . . Well, I'm kind of tired. Think I'll hit the hay. See you in the morning."

Inside his room, Scott grabbed his journal, plopped onto the bed and began to scrawl the feelings that had suddenly changed his perspective on . . . well, everything.

It's finally happened. Part of me feared it would never happen, and part of me dreaded that it would. Oh, but I can't deny that my feelings are overwhelming.

It's alternately the most wonderful and tragic thing that has ever happened to me. I'm so confused and torn. This is so different. I've been involved in so many physical relationships before. But they were so miserably shallow. I think this is the relationship I've been searching for.

Yes, at long last I've fallen in love—head over heels in love! And his name is Dennis.

NINE

Unmasking the Secret

"Tony, I have something to tell you. I've been trying to muster the courage to tell you for some time now. This may come as a shock to you, but I'm gay."

A November wind picked up the words and swept them down the dark and empty beach where Scott rehearsed his speech. The hour was approaching midnight, and Scott walked alone, thinking, ferreting out words, honing sentences, occasionally speaking them aloud.

"Now, before you say anything, let me explain. I've struggled with these feelings ever since I was a kid. I never told anyone because I thought no one would understand. I've felt incredible guilt because I've always been taught being gay was a sin. But now I'm not so sure. I have to be honest with myself. I don't expect you to understand what I'm saying. I just ask you to accept me and remain my friend."

Waves crashed in melodic cadence as Scott walked slowly along the shore. He stopped to throw a stone in the obsidian water.

"I feel secure and comfortable with myself, and it's time to be honest with you. I trust you and I need your support. I've carried this burden by myself long enough. There's something else. I'm seeing someone. Dennis. He's a wonderful, caring person. I know it seems strange, but it isn't really. For me, it's natural, like I've finally found myself. Please understand. I'm not asking for your approval; I've already given that to myself. I'm just tired of pretending. And I wanted you to know."

The night air, chilled by the sea, finally drove Scott toward his car. He negotiated his way through the midnight streets to a tiny one bedroom apartment across town from his parents' home, letting himself in the dark apartment and locking the door behind him. He hit the lights, and suddenly the room was filled with a maze of cardboard boxes and a few odd pieces of misplaced secondhand furniture. Scott was home, in the apartment he'd rented for himself with his last two paychecks from St. Luke's.

It had seemed like a rash decision, made and fulfilled in a matter of weeks. But it wasn't rash at all. Moving out was simply an expression of the rift that had been growing between Scott and his roots for a long, long time. Besides, Scott had just turned twenty-five. He figured it was time he grew up and started living his own life . . . his own way.

Scott emptied the sand from his shoes and collapsed on the floor in front of the TV, the only appliance he'd bothered hooking up so far in his new abode. He sighed. He must have practiced that speech on the beach a thousand times, substituting the names of the people he would be addressing. Joel, Tony, Kirk . . . he'd practiced them all, because these three friends were among the first who needed to know the truth about Scott Cameron.

Scott grabbed the remote and flipped on the TV. The screen brightened onto a sophomoric sitcom in progress. Scott allowed himself to be absorbed by the pabulum on the screen, sitting expressionless despite the prompting of the laugh track. Halfway through the show, the phone rang.

"Scott speaking," he answered an extension laying on the floor within reach. At the same time, he punched the remote and the tube went mute.

"This is Joel. I got your message off the machine. You sounded distraught. Is everything okay?"

Scott looked at his watch. "Okay? Yeah, I guess. Boy, you're sure a night owl. You know it's quarter till one in the morning?"

"Sure, I know. I've been calling you all evening. Did you just get in or something?" Joel asked.

"Yeah. As a matter of fact, I did."

"So was it urgent? You sounded like it was urgent."

"You mean the reason I called?"

"Yep."

"Not urgent, no . . ." Scott's mind reeled back to the words he had fashioned and honed less than an hour ago on a windswept beach. At the moment of truth, they didn't glide out as smoothly as planned. "Joel, there's something I need to tell you. I've wanted to tell you for a long time. This may surprise you. . . ." His voice veered off course and dissolved into silence.

"Okay, so what's the surprise? Lay it on me, Scott."

"You might think this is strange. But to me, it's not strange at all. I haven't told you up until now because I wasn't sure what you'd think." The phone went silent again as Scott groped for a shred of courage, some bristle of strength to carry him through.

"Yes?" Joel prompted.

"What I mean to say is . . . what I'm really trying to tell you . . . is that I have some more money to give you for your missions trip. I, uh, saved some more dimes from my tips before I left Polly's. I'd forgotten about them in the excitement of the new job and all. And then, what with discipleship folding, and we haven't seen too much of each other and all that. . . . Anyway, I've got another hundred dollars or so for you."

"*That's* what all this was about? You weren't sure what I would think about more *dimes?*" Joel was incredulous. "You're a nut, Cameron. Salted, roasted, *and* shelled. An absolute nut."

"You're welcome."

Joel laughed. "Yes, of course, thank you." And then his voice sobered. "You know, you're right. We haven't had much time together. Whaddya say tomorrow we call a few of the guys from the group and plan a little. . . ."

"Get together? Sounds great. But now's probably not the best time for me. In fact, I'm kind of in a hurry right now, but we'll plan something ASAP, okay?"

"Well, sure, I guess. . . ."

"Good to hear your voice, friend. I'll catch you soon."

Scott set the phone receiver in its cradle and paused to think. He closed his eyes, clenched his teeth, and shook his head slightly. Soon, he headed for the kitchen, reached for a bottle of rum in the back of the cupboard, and returned to the couch in the living room. Scott had finally accepted the fact that he was gay; but would his friends be so open-minded?

Scott filled his glass again and again, until at last he passed out in a drunken stupor.

St. Luke's received their first AIDS patient on the Wednesday before Christmas.

Scott learned about William T. Purcell at a morning briefing with the other respiratory therapists in ICU. As usual, Dr. Susannah Patterson conducted the daily meeting, previewing the cases of incoming patients.

On that particular morning, her manner was businesslike, as if to forestall the wave of reaction she anticipated from her staff. She was looking down at her clipboard as she made the announcement, sandwiched in between remarks about an incoming heart transplant and a patient with a gun wound.

She spoke brusquely. "They're sending us an AIDS patient. Probably this afternoon. He'll be on a ventilator for the time being, although traching may be necessary. Full dress—gown, gloves, mask—is recommended for respiratory therapists as well as lab technicians and the nursing staff. Now if there are no questions. . . ."

The year 1982 was drawing to a close, and AIDS had yet to grab the attention of the American public. Even in health care circles, it was a new enemy. But even then, it was an enemy cloaked in mystery and myths . . . and fear.

The reaction was swift. It seemed as if the entire staff began speaking at once.

"I'm not taking care of him . . . no way."

"They don't even know how it's transmitted. If you think I'm going to risk *my* health. . . ."

"I'm a mother—I have small kids. I've got my family to consider."

"No job's worth dying for."

Scott's heart was in his throat. Beneath his starched blue collar, his pulse leapt and danced doubletime in the arteries in his neck. Considering the pounding in his head, he managed to watch the frenzy of his peers with an amazingly cool and distant eye.

Dr. Patterson raised her voice above the din.

"AIDS is *not* transmitted by casual contact," she strained to be heard. "No one's health is being threatened. We simply expect you to take a few minor precautions, then proceed with your jobs as usual."

But no one was listening, and when the staff was dismissed moments later, the frightened men and women left the room buzzing like a hive of angry bees.

Scott spotted Lauren talking with another nurse, standing near the artificial Christmas tree blinking at the entrance to the room that housed the gurneys. As Scott approached, the other nurse turned to leave. Lauren spotted Scott and smiled her brightest. She hoped her hair looked okay.

"Lauren, did you hear?" Scott blurted.

"Hear. . . ."

"About Purcell? The AIDS patient?"

Lauren nodded. "You should have seen the reaction of the other nurses."

"I didn't need to. I saw what the news did to the respiratory therapists."

Lauren bit her lip. "It is sort of scary, isn't it?"

Scott just nodded.

The next day Scott was getting ready to suction the lungs of their newest charge when Lauren entered the room with a new bag of blood for the IV that stood at the edge of the bed. The two friends hardly recognized each other in the green gowns and face shields each wore for protection—theirs or William Purcell's, no one was quite sure.

William Purcell was skeleton thin, fighting pneumonia as

well as the cancer that left his face swollen and blotched with large purple lesions. He was receiving antibiotics, painkillers, and frequent blood infusions, and lay gingerly amid the plastic tubes: two had been inched down his nasal passages; one protruded from his arm. A rectal tube helped control the severe diarrhea he was plagued with.

He was in a light sleep of sorts—a half-consciousness induced by the morphine drip that hung from the IV, next to the blood.

Scott felt his heart wrung like a wet rag inside his chest. He tried to swallow, but his mouth was dry.

Lauren was the first to speak. She shook her head. "Awful way to die," she mused.

Scott nodded. "I'd hate to be in his shoes," was all he finally managed to respond.

Two weeks later, on New Year's Eve, Scott lounged on a black leather couch surrounded by four friends at Dennis's apartment. Memories of the fate he had glimpsed in a hospital bed faded as laughter and banter was lobbed back and forth between the friends. The young men passed around bottles of liquor and chocolate chip cookies laced with marijuana. A stereo blasted out a countdown of the top rock-and-roll hits of the year, and the guys raised their voices to be heard above electric guitar riffs and pounding synthesizers.

"Anybody want a smoke?" offered Brett, a blond with chiseled good looks.

"Go ahead and smoke," Dennis said, "but try to keep the ashes in the ash tray."

"Uh-oh, Mr. Good Housekeeping is back again," Brett snorted.

"Back again? He never left. Dennis has an obsession with cleanliness," Scott said with a laugh. "He scrubs this place to perfection—so it's presentable for the cleaning lady." The friends exploded in laughter.

"Well, cleanliness is next to godliness, right Dennis?" Brett said, giving him a playful shove.

"Speaking of godliness, Scott, what would your church friends think if they knew you were eating pot cookies?" chided a dark-haired man sitting across from Scott.

"They would probably applaud my open-mindedness."

"Yeah, sure they would," the man said sarcastically.

"You know, Scott's not just a churchgoer," Brett leered, "he's a narc, and he's going to bust us for eating these cookies. We better get rid of the evidence, quick." He shoved a whole cookie in his mouth and the guys erupted in laughter again.

"Yeah. Here's his I.D. badge," the dark-haired man added, grabbing Scott's hospital identification from the coffee table. "Says here he's a respiratory tech at St. Luke's. That's a good cover."

"That's right, I am a narc," Scott said. "So pass another cookie and let me eat . . . I mean inspect . . . the evidence."

Around 2:00 a.m., after an evening hallmarked by pot cookies, alcohol, loud music, and laughter, the party broke up and Scott finally headed for home.

"Oh. What the . . . ? All right. Hold on." Scott mumbled in a groggy voice beneath a labyrinth of sheets and blankets. "All right, all right." Massaging a booze-induced headache, he stumbled toward the desk, toward a shrieking, blaring phone somewhere beneath the papers.

"Yeah, this is Scott," he said into the receiver, squinting at his desktop clock. It was 11:30 in the morning, New Year's Day "Oh hi, Tony. . . . No, no, I was awake. I was just lying here. It was just a late night, that's all. I guess it's time to get up anyway. . . . Yeah, I'll be around today. . . . Talk? Sure, what about? Okay, I'll just wait till you get here. . . . Around 3:00? See you then."

Three hours later, Tony sat on the couch, facing Scott. Tony, wearing a white USC sweat shirt and jeans, leaned forward and folded his hands.

"Scott, I know your secret." He looked Scott squarely in the eye, speaking gently but directly. "I know the charade you've been playing. I know what you've been trying to tell me. I know you're gay."

TEN

The Ultimatum

Scott, his face unshaven, hair mussed, stared across at his friend with wide, blood-shot eyes. He stiffened. "What do you mean? What are you saying?"

"Look, Scott, I'm your friend. You don't need to pretend anymore. I know you're gay."

Scott got up from the couch and stood in front of the window. He stroked his whiskered face and gazed out into the street, deserted for the holiday.

This was the moment Scott had dreaded . . . and for which he had hungered. This was the moment of honesty, truth, integrity. This was the moment of wholeness . . . even if the whole Scott had become something no one wanted to recognize; something no one could accept. But maybe wholeness under even conditions like these was better than living a lie.

Scott turned toward Tony and folded his arms. "I'm listening. Tell me more." Scott baited him, gambling that Tony was making a blind accusation.

Tony met the challenge. "I put the pieces together. Every time you talk about problems with relationships, it's always a vague third person reference, like 'they' or 'them.' You're too good a communicator not to say 'she' if you meant 'she.' There were a lot of other clues, like the fact that you've been spending a lot of time with someone named Dennis. The fact that you talk so rarely about girls. The times you've tried to tell me something big, but chickened out at the last minute. I'm not here to condemn you, Scott. I care about you. I want to hear you out on this."

Scott walked back toward the couch. He stood for a moment, evaluating Tony with an intense gaze. The battle, being waged in his soul, raged in his eyes. And then, slowly, Scott sat down in a chair across from his friend. "You're right, Tony. You're right about me."

"I wish you would've told me sooner."

"I was afraid. I didn't know if you'd turn your back on me."

"C'mon, you know me better than that." The two sat in silence for a moment.

"Does anyone else know?" Scott finally asked.

Tony shrugged. "Not for sure. I mean, Caroline and Kirk suspect. I talked to both of them before confronting you. It was something they'd both wondered about already." And then: "Are you happy, Scott?"

"Yes, I am. I mean, it's difficult sometimes, knowing that I'll never get married or have kids—that hurts. I always dreamed of having the perfect family. Life isn't perfect, though, is it?" Scott squared his shoulders. "I went through hell to get where I am today, Tony. And I can finally say I'm comfortable with my life. I like who I am."

"What about this Dennis?" Tony asked.

"Dennis is a guy I've been seeing for a few months now, since August. He's a wonderful, caring person."

"Is it all as great as you're making it sound?" Tony asked quietly.

Scott's face suddenly burned with remembered humiliation as he thought back to the evening, last month, when he walked into Dennis's apartment and found him in bed with someone else. Scott remembered, despite their ongoing relationship, the fact that Dennis never returned Scott's phone calls. Scott thought about the lack of commitment prevalent in the gay community, of the hungry search that seemed to take the men from one lover to the next. He recalled that rejection was as alive and well in the gay community as in any other setting.

Scott cleared his throat. "There are . . . there are difficult aspects."

"Tell me about those," Tony said, his eyes never leaving Scott's.

Scott chewed his lip nervously. In the end he shrugged. "Well . . . like the fact that I'm in a no-win situation with this relationship. If it crashes and burns, as I suspect it probably will, then I've just set myself up for a lot of pain. If, on the other hand, it progresses into something truly special . . . then I would have to come out of the closet. I'd have to make the final choice to abandon my faith, my morals, maybe even my family. I think if I made that choice, it would destroy my parents."

"Just your parents?" Tony asked.

"Whaddya mean?"

"What if it destroyed you, too?"

Scott shuddered. "Look, Tony, I know what I'm doing is wrong. But it's the path I've chosen . . . for now. I know that ultimately, I'll have to reap what I'm sowing, and that's scary. But I don't have the faith or the courage or the discipline to live the 'good life' right now. Maybe someday . . . but not right now."

"Scott, no one does . . . by themselves. That's why you should have told. . . ."

Scott wasn't listening. "You know, I hate it when people say you can't be Christian and gay—because I'm convinced you can be. At the same time, I know I won't be entirely happy until I've totally renounced the gay life and turned to Him. But . . . but I *can't.* I have to examine and pursue this side of my life, or I'll never really know who I am."

Tony groaned. "Scott, everyone has a dark side. It's that old sin nature' thing. It's there, in every one of us. My struggle doesn't happen to be homosexuality, but we've all got our struggles. Sometimes we win the struggle. And sometimes we lose. But just because the struggle is there doesn't mean we're destined to give in to it. Knowing we aren't alone—knowing we're accountable to other Christians who love us—that's the thing that gets us off our butts and back on track. It doesn't happen overnight; sometimes we march back to the right path, and sometimes we crawl, taking months and even years. But we're never alone. You don't have to do it alone, Scott."

"You don't understand, Tony," Scott said in a voice so low it was barely audible. "I *am* alone. I'm frightened, and I'm alone. But I'm where I have to be right now. I'm discovering things about myself that I have to know to live out the rest of my life."

Knowing that Kirk Graham suspected the truth, Scott spent several days gathering his nerve, then called his old friend. Kirk's response was not unlike that of Tony. Kirk was confused, concerned, and supportive. He didn't pretend to have any solutions, although he told Scott repeatedly that he wished he did.

For Scott, the end of a decade of silence was . . .

. . . anticlimactic.

He wrote in his journal:

Somehow, I always expected a big reaction, the burst of the bombshell. But it wasn't like that at all. After all these years, finally letting go of my most closely guarded secret . . . and what emerged was a few calm chats. I wasn't judged, or misjudged. I didn't detect any condemnation or rejection. That's much more than I expected.

Although . . . both Tony and Kirk seem to think this is just a phase I'm going through. They may not be judgmental, but they sure don't understand where I'm at.

Maybe time will give my friends a chance to see that I'm still me—that while being gay affects every area of my life, it doesn't make up all of who I am.

They'll never understand, really. How could they?

But at least I'm not so alone anymore.

There's hope now.

Valentine's Day signaled the demise of Dennis.

Driving across town to Dennis's apartment, Scott's thoughts seemed as cloudy as the February sky overhead. He thought about his Christian friends, about his unfulfilling relationship with Dennis, about the chasm in his own soul despite his newfound acceptance of his homosexuality. His thoughts mirrored his latest journal entry, written that very morning:

For so long I hid my true feelings from my friends, but now that they know and seem to be accepting . . . I'm not convinced my feelings are right.

I feel Dennis withdrawing and that scares me. I don't know where he's at with our relationship. . . . Gay men seem to be so non-committal. They move from relationship to relationship. I want a lasting love. . . . I'm disillusioned. My attempts to talk seriously with Dennis have repeatedly been rebuffed. Today, maybe today, we can settle things.

"Oh, Scott, come on in," Dennis said flatly. He threw the door open as he turned and walked toward the kitchen, leaving Scott standing in the doorway. "Well, c'mon in."

"Hardly a warm reception from someone I haven't seen for a week and a half," Scott said, closing the door behind him and throwing his duffel bag on the couch where it dislodged a pillow "Look. Is everything okay? Did I come at a bad time? You said on the phone it would be all right to come over."

"Yeah, everything's fine, Scott," Dennis crouched beneath the sink, reaching for tile cleanser.

"I was hoping maybe we could talk about a few things."

Dennis scrubbed the sink with the coarse side of the sponge. He turned on the faucet and wrung out the sponge, watching a small stream trickle into the sink. "Oh, didn't I tell you, Scott? I've got to go to San Diego tonight. I've got to shower, pack, and leave by 6:00. Something just came up."

"No, you didn't tell me. You could have mentioned that on the phone before I drove over. Is this business or pleasure?"

Dennis strolled past Scott toward the bedroom. He stopped to stare absentmindedly at Scott's duffel bag on the couch. Dennis picked it up, dropped in onto the floor, and realigned the pillows.

"Business."

"Well, what am I supposed to do?" Scott snapped. "I just got here."

"Gerald is having Brett over for a burger and a soak in the jacuzzi. Maybe you could join them." Dennis pulled a suitcase from the hall closet, sidled into the bedroom, and closed the door.

Three hamburgers later, Scott rested both elbows on the rim of the jacuzzi, flung his head back and stared up into the night sky, putting the finishing touches on his new resolve: Dennis was history.

Who needed him? Who needed that kind of treatment? For the first time in a long time, Scott felt his life was starting to come together. Maybe it was possible to be a Christian and live the kind of life he wanted. After all, Kirk and Tony knew the "big secret," and the world hadn't come to an end. Maybe Scott was finally learning to live with himself. Now all he needed was to find someone he could love . . . who could love him back. And even Scott could see that Dennis wasn't a logical candidate. Dennis wasn't ready for a real relationship; and Scott wasn't ready for a simple affair.

Gerald, sitting several feet away in the bubbling water, was finishing a Coors. His pony-tailed hair was slick from the water and shiny from the yellow lights surrounding the spa. "Now this is the California life," Gerald crushed the can in his fist and tossed it noisily onto the cement. "A cold beer, a hot tub, good friends . . . under the stars in February. Do you realize the rest of the country is still snowed in?"

Brett nodded at Scott. "We like to use the jacuzzi this time of year. A lot of privacy. No one else in the apartment complex uses it in the winter."

The three sat listening to the sloshing of water and the hum of water jets. A thumbnail moon peeked out from behind heavy clouds, casting silvery flakes on the tumbling water. The bubbling jacuzzi steamed like a boiling teapot.

"Gerald, your dad's a pastor, right?" Scott said, breaking the silence with something remembered from a conversation with Dennis.

Gerald nodded.

"Does he know you're gay?"

"No way! I moved out here from Wyoming to go to school," he replied. "My parents aren't close enough to check up on me. Why cause a big hassle by telling them? My old man would have a coronary if he knew about my lifestyle. What about you? Your parents know?"

Scott shook his head vehemently. "Just a couple of friends from church. No one else . . . from the straight side of my life, I mean."

Gerald seemed interested. "And? What happened when you told them?"

"They took it pretty well, I guess, but they keep saying it's just a phase. They think I'm confused right now, and I'll get over it. They said they're praying for me."

"Just shine 'em on, Cameron," Brett piped in.

Gerald shot him a halting look. The threesome fell silent for several minutes. Soon Brett hopped out of the water and, dripping, fumbled through a gym bag lying a few feet away.

Brett walked back and sat down on the edge of the jacuzzi, feet dangling in the water. He held three more cans of beer and a plastic bag of pills. He popped open the cans and handed them to Gerald and Scott. He carefully dried his hand on the towel beside him and extracted a small yellow pill from the bag.

"Would anyone care to join me . . ." He stopped, looked around, and lowered his voice. "Would anyone care to join me in some speed? All this talk about parents and crap is bringing me down. But this should pick up our little party."

He threw Scott the towel to dry his hands, then handed him a pill.

The sun filtered through venetian blinds, creating streams of light against darkened walls in Scott's bedroom. Beneath the second-story window, on the gray concrete walkway, sat the Thursday *L. A. Times* morning edition. A jogger, togged in blue sweats and headphones, bounced silently by. A school bus shifted gears, roaring down Colorado Avenue, which was relatively empty now that the morning rush hour had subsided. Inside Scott's room, the clock radio flashed 9:13 a.m. and the thermostat kicked in and blew warm air into the room. Scott rustled contentedly under an electric blanket.

Across the room, the phone rang and shattered the sweet silence. Scott, ripped from a heavy sleep, threw back the covers and leaped to his feet.

"Yeah, hello?"

"Scott, this is Tony. Sounds like you're still asleep. Did I wake you?"

"Yeah, sort of. Hey, Tony, hold a minute." Scott set down the phone and rubbed the sleep from his eyes. He took a deep breath and resumed the conversation. "Okay, what's up?"

"Scott, I'd like to get together with you. Kirk, too."

"Kirk too?" Scott repeated, still clearing the sleep from his thoughts. "What's up?"

"You free tonight?" Tony evaded the question.

"Tonight? Yeah, I think so. Yeah, I'm free."

"Great. We were thinking about a pizza, around seven o'clock at Kirk's folks' place. We'll catch a movie after we eat. You can come?"

"Sure. I guess."

Scott hung up the phone and climbed back into bed. He pulled the electric blanket up around his neck and flipped over on his side. A truck rumbled down the street as Scott closed his eyes and burrowed deeper—a small attempt to shut himself off from the rest of the world.

At 7:05 that evening, Scott turned his car into the affluent neighborhood on the east end of town where Kirk's parents owned their home. Scott remembered the summer—it seemed like a decade ago—when he and Kirk had been so close. Scott had spent long hours at the Graham household: swimming, watching videos, making sandwiches in Mrs. Graham's country kitchen. But now, as he pulled into the circular driveway behind Kirk's Toyota and killed the engine, the house loomed unfamiliar changed somehow. Scott shrugged off the feeling, knowing the house was solid and that the changes existed solely in the heart of the beholder.

An hour later, the three friends lounged around the kitchen table, overlooking the remains of a thick-crust bell pepper and pepperoni pizza, extra large. Scott stretched, one hand on his stomach. "Great meal," he said. Glancing at Kirk, he added, "Got a newspaper around? Let's see what's playing at the mall."

Tony cleared his throat. "There'll be time for that. Before we see a movie, I wanted to say something."

Suddenly Kirk lowered his eyes to the table. Scott caught the movement and threw a suspicious glance toward Tony. "Yeah? What about?"

"Scott, it's like this. I know you say you're comfortable with who you are. I mean with being homosexual and everything. . . ."

Scott groaned. "So that was the whole reason for inviting. . . ."

"Don't cut me off, Scott," Tony interrupted, raising his voice. "Hear me out on this. I know what you say about your experience. But experience isn't the final word. The Bible is. And what the Bible says is clear. You're sinning, Scott."

Scott sighed. "I thought you guys were okay with this. I thought we had agreed to disagree."

"Not exactly," Tony said. "Look, as a brother in Christ, I've got a responsibility to try to see you restored, just like it says in Matthew 18:15. Here." Tony bent, reaching to the floor beside his chair. When he sat up, he held a Bible. Scott eyed his friend coolly as Tony flipped quickly toward the back of his Bible, stopping in the book of Matthew.

Tony read, "If your brother sins, go and show him his fault, just between the two of you. If he listens to you, you have won your brother over. But if he will not listen, take one or two others along, so that every matter may be established by the testimony of two or three witnesses. If he refuses to listen to them, tell it to the church; and if he refuses to listen even to the church, treat him as you would a pagan."

"That's great, Tony," Scott said dryly. "But I'm not as convinced as you are that the Bible's such an open-and-shut case against homosexuality."

Tony stared at his friend. "What about Romans 1 where it talks about men abandoning natural relations with women and burning with lust for each other?"

Kirk, still staring at the table, sank lower in his chair.

Scott shook his head. "It's only unnatural if you're heterosexual, Tony. But I've had these feelings a long, long time—since I was a kid, so it's not unnatural for me at all. That verse is talking about heterosexuals who abandon natural relationships, not born homosexuals."

Tony's voice was strained. "You're deceived, man. You're really deceived."

"The thing about homosexuality that's wrong is the promiscuous sex," Scott hurried on. "But if you're exclusive with one person, then it's okay. It's like marriage."

"You believe that?" Tony steamed. "Okay. Are you going to marry someone?"

"Look, Tony. I didn't mean it so literally. It's just a piece of paper, you know."

"The Bible says sex belongs in marriage. And if the government says you need a marriage certificate to be married, you'd darn well better get one. If not, you're in violation of Romans 13," Tony raved. "Besides, when this relationship doesn't work out and you go to other men, is that immorality? What keeps you in that marriage bond? And what are the grounds for divorce? If you are going to apply the same rules as if it were a marriage between a man and a woman, you can't change some of the rules just because it's a gay relationship."

Kirk looked up for the first time. His eyes were pained. "Tony's right, man. You're hurting yourself. The Bible's pretty clear on homosexuality. I mean, the entire cities of Sodom and Gomorrah were destroyed because of the homosexuality there."

"You don't understand, Kirk," Scott said, his voice raised with frustration. "They were destroyed because of the sin of inhospitality, not homosexuality."

Tony laughed then. A clipped laugh marbled with anger. "You've bought into it all, haven't you? There's no use arguing with you. No use sitting here while you bend scriptures."

"Oh no?" Scott glowered at his friend.

"No. You're going to do this apart from what the Bible says. That's clear to me. Which takes us right back to Matthew 18. Here we are: the two witnesses confronting you about your sin. Now we've got to take this before the church, and you've got a choice to make, Scott. If you don't make the right one, it's gonna come down to cutting you off from the church."

Scott felt the anger and hurt swell in his chest. "You trapped me. Both of you." He whipped his head to look at Kirk, too. "You invited me here for pizza, and suddenly here you are doing the second step of Matthew 18. Deception doesn't create a real good environment for repentance, guys." Suddenly Scott's chair scraped against the floor tile as he pushed back roughly from the table.

"Scott, wait," Tony entreated with his eyes. "This is serious stuff. I just don't want you to live like this. I don't want you to die of AIDS."

Scott stood, grabbing his keys from the table. His face was flushed with anger. "Thanks for the food and fellowship," he said with a sarcastic edge. "Just like old times." He turned and stormed from the kitchen.

Tony and Kirk sat in silence as the front door closed with a slam. Kirk sat with his elbows on the table, his face buried in his hands. Tony stared out the kitchen window into the night, his heart a battleground as his feelings warred between anger and guilt.

Somehow, the evening hadn't turned out like he had planned.

One Wednesday night, toward the end of March, Scott got off work at eleven. He grabbed his jacket from the lunch room, said goodnight to the incoming staff, and headed for the elevator. Downstairs in the lobby, he nodded a greeting toward the receptionist. Moments later he punched the release bar on a set of double-doors at the rear of the hospital and exited into brisk darkness.

The night air splashed cool on his face. Scott, his jacket

swinging open, savored the drop in temperature. He gazed skyward. The stars were hidden tonight by a canopy of clouds, dusky gray against the midnight black of the heavens.

Halfway across the darkened parking lot, Scott slowed his pace. His eyes narrowed. Without thinking, he assumed a defensive posture, slipping his hands inside his jacket pockets and tightening his jaw.

Kirk Graham was sitting in his truck, parked next to Scott's Mustang.

The friends had spoken only briefly since the "pizza" night at Kirk's house. And even those moments of communication had seemed strained. Kirk climbed out of the truck and waited as Scott approached.

"Well, Kirk, what are you doing here?" Scott said evenly.

Kirk shrugged. "Knew you'd be getting off work and I needed to talk to you."

"So talk."

"I'll shoot straight with you, Scott. I'm . . . I'm between a rock and a hard place here."

Scott leaned against the bed of Kirk's Toyota pickup and folded his arms.

"This isn't easy for me," Kirk continued. "But I need to let you know. Tony has given me, well, an ultimatum. He says he won't be in my wedding if you're in it."

"Why?" Scott asked through a tight jaw, feeling the heat rising in him. It wasn't a necessary question—but Scott wanted to hear the words. He wanted to make Kirk say them. Aloud. What he *really* wanted was for the words to turn to stone in Kirk's throat.

"Why? He's sort of saying that the church isn't doing anything, so he has to take a stand. He figures you've pretty much made your decision about being gay, but none of the church leaders are confronting you about it."

"That's not true. A pastor and one of the elders. . . ."

"Scott, they met with you once and then they let it drop," Kirk said. "You told me yourself you never called the pastor back like he wanted you to—and he never called you. Don't you see?

The church doesn't know how to handle you. So they're just ignoring you, hoping the whole thing just goes away."

"Yeah. Everyone except Tony." Scott's mouth twisted as he formed the bitter words.

"I'm sorry, Scott, I really am. The point is, I'm getting caught in the middle here."

"I've been your friend for years, and now you're letting him pressure you into this."

"Scott, it's biblical. You know that. Tony says you've got to be . . . cut off."

"Cut off? Like what, Kirk? Like a cancer? Like a wart?" Scott spit the words at Kirk. "Or maybe cut *out* is a better word. Cut out like a heart. Maybe like the heart of a friend who loved you."

"Scott, that's not what I. . . ."

"Look. I'll make it easy on you, Kirk," Scott shuddered, suddenly very, very tired. He hid his face in his palms a moment before continuing. "Let's just say I bow out, okay? I'm out of the wedding. That should make everyone happy."

Kirk watched as Scott climbed into his car, fired up the engine and sped, tires screaming, from the hospital lot.

At 11:45, Tony Lozano dialed Scott's number for the third time in fifteen minutes. He knew the number by heart. Scott, fingering his keys just outside the door to his apartment, heard the phone. He didn't rush to catch it.

Tony counted the rings. On the sixteenth ring, Scott answered with a foul-sounding "Hello?"

Tony told Scott that he really cared . . . that he grieved for Scott and wanted him to come back to the fold. Tony explained that he just couldn't have anything to do with Scott until that happened. He quoted Scripture, assuring Scott there was no malice or cruelty involved, but that Scott's lifestyle left no alternative except for Scott to be cut off from fellowship. Tony added that he loved Scott; he was doing this for Scott's good.

By the time Scott hung up the phone, he sat shaking his head at himself. Tony was good. Real good. Tony actually believed all the stuff he was saying, and for that Scott hated him just a little bit less. The pastor and the elder from church had seemed compassionate, but the lack of a prior relationship with the two men had made Scott feel awkward and distant. Then there was Kirk. Scott winced at the thought of his long-time friend. Scott wondered if he would ever forgive Kirk Graham.

A spring wind gusted around the building where Scott sat on the floor in his apartment, mulling over a life gone askew. Scott thought to himself that he had learned one lesson in the past weeks, and learned it good: no more baring his soul to his straight friends.

There was a moment, just a moment, when he grappled with thoughts of his parents, and of his grandmother, and he wished he could tell them all exactly what it was he was dealing with: the struggles and disappointments, the few victories, the tears.

But I can't. I could never do that to them—the pain, the disappointment, the agonizing over things they couldn't change. It's my problem, not theirs.

Sadly I'm afraid they'll never know who I really am, after all. . . .

Scott climbed to his feet and staggered, exhausted in heart more than body, to his bed. But before he succumbed to sleep, he came to a second conclusion.

Before he locked himself forever behind the iron walls of secrecy, there was one more person he needed to tell.

A Friend Is Born for Adversity

T ammy Cameron Hadley, two months pregnant, carried a beach chair and a handful of magazines from the two-bedroom rental she shared with Mitch and dumped them in the trunk of her Mazda. She slammed the lid of the trunk. Suddenly she remembered something, and hurried back toward the house. She returned a moment later with an extra sweat shirt. It was a Saturday in early April, and the beach could be downright chilly at this time of year.

Just then, muffled and distant, she heard a phone ring.

She paused at the curb, debating whether to let it go or dash madly toward the house. After the third ring she made a run for it, fumbling for the house key as she scurried.

In his apartment across town, Scott's jaw was clenched as he listened to the repeated rings echoing in Tammy's empty house.

Brrrrrrng. . . .

Scott drummed his fingers on his desk.

Brrrrrrng. . . .

This was torture.

Brrrrrrng. . . .

With a potent mixture of relief and dread at the delay of the inevitable, Scott lowered the receiver from his ear. But before it hit the cradle he heard a voice, breathless and small, "Hello. Hello?"

He paused for just a moment, debating, and then lifted the phone back to his ear. "Hello, Tammy?"

"Oh, Scott, it's you. You came *this* close to missing me. But I'm glad you didn't. I've been meaning to call you."

Scott's heart plummeted. So Tammy had already heard. . . .

Tammy bubbled on. "There's this girl at my work I want you to meet. She's got a great personality, Scott. Now *don't* say a thing: I know that when people start hyping a personality, it usually means the person's bankrupt in the looks department. But not so this time. Anyway, I told her all about you. And she wants to meet you. Her name is Gloria. I can give you her number, or I can talk to her Monday at work and set. . . ."

"Thanks, Tammy. Really. But maybe some other time."

For the first time, Tammy heard the edginess in her brother's voice. "You sound depressed again," she said. "Depressed or uptight, I can't tell which."

Scott cleared his throat. "There's something we've got to talk about."

"Right now?" Tammy peered out the kitchen window at her Mazda, loaded up for the surf. "I'm on my way to meet Caroline. We're going to the beach." Tammy's face brightened. "Wanna come? Can we talk there?"

"Caroline Lozano? No. No way. Tony and I had a . . . a falling out and I can't see Caroline."

Tammy's eyes narrowed in thought. "Really? Okay. Just let me call Caroline and tell her I'll be a little late. I'm coming over."

Driving to Scott's, Tammy considered the possibilities. What had come between Scott and Tony? Money? Nah. Could Scott be in some kind of trouble with the law? Tammy's brow twisted in thought. Even if Scott were in legal trouble, Tammy doubted that could cause a rift between the long-time friends. No, it had to be something shocking. Something entirely unpalatable to Tony Lozano that would cause him to ban Scott from his life. Tammy could think of only two potential unforgivables: Scott was gay, or he had made a pass at Tony's wife. Tammy knew Scott wasn't gay. He probably made a pass at Caroline.

At that moment, Tammy remembered a conversation she'd

had with Mitch, almost six months earlier. They'd been sitting at the kitchen table over plates of Tammy's lasagna, and somehow the conversation had touched on Scott's frequent moodiness.

Mitch had made a comment—one that had infuriated his new bride. Tammy had dismissed the words at the time and nursed a smidgeon of anger at Mitch for the good part of a week.

The words, nearly forgotten, came back to haunt her as she pulled into the driveway of Scott's apartment. *You know, Tammy, I don't think Scott is as moral as he wants everyone to believe.*

Scott met Tammy at the door. "Come in."

Tammy sat on the couch, her eyes never leaving Scott's. She watched him and waited. Scott sat down in a chair, then stood again, chewing his lip nervously.

"Scott, why am I here?" she finally asked.

"I'm in a relationship, Tammy. And I don't think . . . well, that Mom and Dad would approve."

A single question formed on Tammy's tongue. Then all at once, the question was unnecessary—Tammy knew the answer. "Is it a woman, Scott?"

"No."

"Then it's a man."

Scott swallowed. "Yes. It's a man."

Tammy, her head swimming, stalled for time to think. "I'm . . . I'm surprised, Scott."

"I figured you would be." Scott watched his sister carefully for her next response. When she remained silent, he continued: "Tony and Caroline know about it all. And Kirk. And the pastor. Now that the pastor knows, I figure it'll be a matter of weeks before the world knows—even though I'm going to do what I can to keep the whole thing under wraps. I didn't want you to have to deal with this, Tammy. I never wanted anyone I loved to have to deal with this."

Tammy sighed. "I think that's what love *is*, Scott. Sharing the good and sharing the bad. For better or for worse. Am I right?"

Scott just shrugged. "The point is, it's all hitting the fan now."

"What about Mom and Dad?" Tammy's eyes widened. "Are you telling Mom and Dad?"

When Scott looked up, the wounds of his heart were reflected in his eyes. "I'm . . . I'm not sure. That's the worst of it, Tammy. Telling Mom and Dad. It's one thing to lose the love of friends like Tony and Kirk—and Joel. I don't think Joel knows yet, but I can imagine his response." Scott buried his face in his hands. "He told me about a friend he had once . . . a friend who had been gay. The friend wasn't even gay anymore, Tammy. I mean he'd gone straight, or celibate, or whatever it is gay people do with their feelings once they decide to reclaim their lives. But Joel couldn't even handle *that*. It destroyed the friendship. I can't imagine what he'll feel toward me when he learns the truth."

"About Mom and Dad . . ." Tammy reminded softly.

Scott groaned. "What should I do, Tammy? Tell me what I should do."

Tammy looked down at her hand, resting protectively on the imperceptible swell of her body where a new life lay nestled. She thought of the safety of the womb, and how it was contrasted by the stark realities of the world into which her baby would be born.

Scott was waging war with hell itself as he struggled to define, and even accept, himself in light of his twisted desires. And once Gail and Chuck knew, the entire family could be torn asunder . . . loved ones living on opposite sides of a deep rift—opposite sides of a canyon—created by Scott's homosexuality, just as Scott's homosexuality had created a chasm in his very own soul.

Tammy thought she was probably being selfish, but she didn't want that kind of a beginning for the son or daughter she was nurturing with her very flesh. Her little one would discover the harsh realities of life soon enough. For the time of the baby's birth, and maybe just a little while longer, Tammy wanted her family to be . . . well, a *family*, untouched by the stains of Scott's secret . . . of Scott's choices.

Tammy looked up at her brother. "Maybe wait. Maybe just until the baby . . ." her voice trailed off.

Scott nodded. "I understand."

They talked a short while longer, until Tammy had to leave to meet Caroline Lozano.

"I know I'm probably wasting my breath," Scott said as he walked Tammy to her car, "but you don't have to make *me* the topic of conversation all day today with Caroline, you know."

"You provide me with the best gossip I've heard in a month of Sundays, and you expect me to keep quiet?" Tammy quipped, for the moment her light tone helping to neutralize the impact of Scott's news.

"Well, it was a thought."

"Scott," Tammy asked, suddenly curious, "are you going to wear an earring?"

Scott laughed. "No."

"Can I ask you one more question?"

"Sure."

"What happens if you're in a crowd and someone starts telling 'gay' jokes?"

Scott shrugged. "I guess I'll laugh if they're funny."

Lauren spot-checked the patients at half past the hour. She was cordial—warm even—plumping pillows, checking charts, all the while generous with the little compliments and words of encouragement that shed more than a little sunshine in the cold corridors of St. Luke's.

But she was distracted, scanning the hallway as she walked between rooms, checking her watch occasionally, wondering if her lipstick was on straight.

Darn it all. Lauren knew the symptoms. She had fallen victim to—of all things!—a serious case of infatuation.

She was standing at the nurses' module, bent over a file cabinet, when she heard his voice. She kept her eyes on the file tabs, letting her russet-blonde locks fall forward to hide the small smile she harbored.

Scott greeted Glenda first and then his boss, Nick, who was lifting a box of paper supplies from a top cabinet for Glenda, his firm biceps bulging beneath the sleeves of his green scrub shirt. When Scott saw Lauren, he sneaked up behind her and gave her a quick nuzzle at the back of the neck. Lauren turned, but Scott was gone, on to his next patient.

Nick followed suit, answering the pager he wore on his belt. Lauren closed the file drawer and looked up to find the module deserted except for Glenda, who was watching her with hawk-eyes.

"What?" Lauren asked. "Is there ink on my face or something?"

Glenda smiled. "No. But your head is thicker than the walls in x-ray."

Lauren raised her eyebrows. "What's that supposed to mean?"

"Scott."

Lauren sighed. "Oh. *That* again."

"Lauren, believe me. In fact, let's bet on it. I'll bet a hundred dollars that I'm right."

"And I'll bet my heart that you're wrong."

"You aren't talking hypothetical—are you, Lauren?" Glenda asked, a note of sympathy in her husky voice. "Your heart's already on the line."

Lauren lowered her eyes. "I'm falling in love with him, Glenda. It's awful."

"They say loving a gay man is a special kind of hell."

"He's *not* gay, Glenda. And please stop saying he is. He can't be. He just can't be."

"Oh?" Glenda's voice traveled up an octave. "Then what's so awful about falling in love with him? If *he's* straight, why are *you* miserable?"

Lauren sighed. "As far as he's concerned, we're more . well, *friends* than anything else. I mean, we date a lot—movies, dinner, renting videos, shopping at the mall—but it's not like. . "

"Like?" Glenda prompted.

". . . like . . ." Lauren searched for just the right word.

"Not like what? Lovers? Not like dating? Not like there's chemistry? I know: Maybe it's not even like a man and a woman. . . ."

"Knock it off," Lauren's sea-blue eyes blazed and her anger made the color rise to her cheeks. "Just knock it off."

Scott's work shift and Lauren's ended about eleven that night, and as they often did, the two struck off for an all-night coffee shop somewhere for a piece of pie and some small talk. Around midnight, Scott walked Lauren to her car and opened the door for her. He leaned forward and planted a quick peck on her lips. And then he was gone.

Lauren called it the peck and run. It was a standard feature of their times together, although occasionally it was replaced by the hug and run. Lauren grumbled to herself as she shifted into reverse and prepared to back out of her parking space. Scott wasn't gay. She knew he wasn't gay. Okay, so she thought he wasn't gay.

As for the peck and run routine, she figured Scott was probably just a little shy when it came to physical intimacy.

At that very moment, Scott was speeding down a deserted avenue, heading for a midnight rendezvous with a friend just getting off work himself. Gary Anderson was a registered nurse working nights on a psychiatric ward in a neighboring facility. He and Scott had met last month at a gay bar in L.A., and the two had been lovers ever since.

One Sunday afternoon in early June, Tony Lozano phoned Scott at home. Scott groaned inwardly when he heard the familiar voice belonging to the one-time friend whose memory had fueled much bitterness and hurt.

But Tony, undaunted by Scott's cool greeting, launched straight into an apology for the events of several months ago, when he had helped set into motion the confrontations that sealed Scott's exit from the church. Tony asked Scott if their friendship could be rebuilt, despite the fact that Tony still decried the gay lifestyle.

"I hate what you're doing, Scott," Tony said. "And it really bugged me that the church has been teaching us all along how to handle unrepentant sin in the life of a brother, but when push came to shove, no one was willing to step out and deal with you about your life."

"You seemed to do okay," Scott couldn't refrain from the jibe.

"I was too harsh, Scott. I was long on discipline and short on compassion."

Scott absorbed the apology, thinking. "So why the change of heart?"

Tony rushed to answer, his excitement showing. "I read in Proverbs—about a brother being born for adversity. And I thought, that's you and me. You're up to your neck in adversity and trouble, even if you aren't willing to admit it. But I still care about you. I'm still going to do everything I can to help you see that the lifestyle you're in now is destroying you . . . but that's difficult to do when we aren't even speaking to each other."

Scott was cynical. "Look, Tony. I'll be honest here. Since my conversation with the pastor, the closest I've come to church has been when Gary and I argue about the meaning of God."

"Gary?" Tony repeated.

"He's a . . . friend."

"You argue often?" Tony asked.

"Often enough," Scott admitted. "Gary has a rather eclectic perspective on religion. He's into New Age philosophies, meditation, herb healers, and reading karmas."

"So if you aren't going to church yourself, Scott, why do you and Gary clash?" Tony asked. "Why not just agree with him?"

At that point Scott managed to change the subject. But deep inside, he knew the answer to Tony's question. He knew that despite his professed acceptance of his homosexuality, Scott's soul still harbored a remnant of faith . . . a gnawing of conviction . . . a stirring of hope.

These were the very things that drove him into his defense of Jesus Christ whenever Gary felt the urge to play the Devil's advocate.

At Tony's offer of friendship, Scott felt the tremors of faith, conviction and hope, stronger than usual—but not quite strong enough to rattle the door of the stronghold he had built around his heart.

In June, Scott finally gave in and accepted an invitation to Tony and Caroline's house for pizza. The evening was strained, but bearable.

A few weeks later, Scott agreed to go to a movie with Tammy and Caroline; Tony decided to join the party at the last minute. Scott concluded that the evening was almost fun.

Shortly after that, there was another dinner at the Lozano home, and Scott came away feeling almost—but not quite—close again to Tony.

It was about that time that Scott realized something: Tony Lozano wasn't running from Scott's secret. But neither was he accepting it. Tony was battling Scott's homosexuality with everything he had: friendship, love, prayers, compassion . . . and plenty of hard words about the hell-bent path Scott had accepted as his own.

But Tony was *there.* Scott, the man, hadn't been rejected along with the sin.

It was the exact kind of response—the exact kind of love— that Scott had yearned for in those first years of fighting his temptation tooth and nail. In those first years—when every trip to a gay bar or bath, every one-night stand, every lusty party left him devastated over his failings—Scott had prayed for a friend like Tony.

If only Tony had known the truth *then* . . . but Scott hadn't given him the chance. Scott hadn't given *anyone* the chance. . . .

Now? Now Tony was great. It was just that Scott didn't need the guidance anymore. At one time Scott had battled the temptations; but he'd lost *that* battle long before Tony showed up to help.

Now Scott's struggle was simply this: to reconcile his lusts and loves with the stubborn faith in God that, somehow, he just couldn't seem to shake.

TWELVE

Piecing Together the Puzzle

S eptember dawned in a blaze, breaking the standing heatwave records with parching Santa Ana winds blowing in from the south. Scott, having completed his two-year respiratory therapy program at City College, registered at the school for a couple of evening writing classes. He wanted to finally get that BA in journalism he had started toward at Western Christian College. How long ago had it been since he was there? He knew what it *felt* like . . . and it felt like an entire lifetime ago.

Not that he especially needed more practice when it came to writing. By now Scott's stash of journals had grown until it threatened the sides of the cardboard box that housed the books under his bed. That summer he had written:

I still have aspirations of being a successful journalist. I think there should be at least one good novel lying somewhere within me. Who knows? Maybe I'll write a book about an AIDS patient.

It would be a chance to express what it's like to be different, and yet . . . not too unlike everyone else. The fears, the disappointment, the loneliness—even the ultimate triumph . . . and the ultimate loss. It needs to be told.

I just hope it doesn't turn out to be autobiographical.

A few nights later Scott awoke in the middle of the night, his bedroom far too hot for sleeping. A half-dozen hours earlier, city thermometers had registered 102 degrees, and the night air hadn't done a whole lot to remedy the situation.

Hoping to find a cooling breeze, Scott drew back the curtains from his open window. On a whim, he flipped the small latches that held the screen in place, lowering it to his bedroom floor. Scott leaned out into the darkness. It was, as he had hoped, refreshing on his bare skin.

And the stars . . . God, the stars.

Scott stared across the heavens and marveled at God's showpieces there: Orion's belt, the Big Dipper and the Little Dipper, the North Star, and more. All visible. All shimmering, glimmering—God's jewels against black velvet.

Leaning on his elbows, absorbing starlight and the faint chill of the night, Scott began to pray.

Not for himself . . . Scott figured it was probably too late for that.

Instead, he prayed for Tammy and the baby that was due in roughly three months—his little niece or nephew.

Scott suspected he would never know the joys of family life firsthand. But that wasn't the worst of it: he often wondered if he would ever know the joys of a forever love. As usual, the fears had found their way into the pages of his journals:

I ache to find a lover. Not just a lover of my body—because I'm becoming more convinced than ever that sex without love is worthless—but a lover of my mind, of my personality, of my soul. Perhaps I'll never find him—or her. Perhaps part of my lot in life is to learn to live without ever having my heart's desire.

Perhaps . . . but I can still hope. I think as long as there's a little spark of life left, I'll still hope.

Scott had spent a lifetime searching, and sometimes the thing he sought seemed about as reachable as the stars in a windswept midnight heaven. He thought to himself that he would give anything, short of his soul, to find a relationship like that. Short of his soul? He shook his head. He had probably come close to forfeiting that already. There were those who would say he already had. . . .

His thoughts waned and wandered like the night air that washed his body in cool waves. *Sometimes I think my only real comfort in life will be my writing. Perhaps, someday, my writing will be considered beautiful and moving because it was born out of pain and tragic loss.*

How much better it would have been, I think, to have had inspiration spring from love and fulfillment. . . .

In the end, he looked one last time at the stars winking at him from their inaccessible heights, then drew the curtains and went back to bed, vague thoughts of life and purpose and love still stirring slightly in his head.

In mid-November, Scott came down with the flu. He pulled the phone to the table at his bedside, right next to the can of 7-Up and the Saltine crackers. First he called his boss, Nick, with the news. Then, nestling deeper beneath the blankets, he redialed the hospital and got Lauren on the phone. They talked for several minutes, and before they hung up, Lauren had promised to come by the following day with a pot of homemade chicken noodle soup.

Around noon the next day, Lauren knocked on the door to Scott's apartment. She knocked gingerly, balancing a warm kettle beneath her other arm. Lauren's curiosity swelled like a small tide. Seeing Scott at home would be a first: He had made it clear from the beginning that he liked his privacy. A moment later Scott answered the door wearing a pair of sweats and a pallid complexion.

Lauren didn't waste any time, taking the soup into the kitchen and opening cupboards to find a bowl. She found cups . . . she found cereal. . . .

"Scott, where do you keep your bowls?" she hollered into the living room where Scott had returned to a nest of pillows and blankets strewn over the couch.

"Above the silverware drawer," he called back with as much energy as he could muster. Even so, the words barely reached Lauren.

"Silverware drawer," Lauren muttered. "Now where the heck's that?"

Suddenly the front door swung open. Lauren, still in the kitchen with her back to the door, felt a cool gust of November air blow into the apartment. Someone said, "I'm back. No, don't get up. I'll just put these away."

Lauren turned to face the voice. It was a man, in his early thirties, blond and tall with well-built thighs. He wore navy sweat pants and a white sweat shirt with a blue and gold emblem above the left breast. He held a laundry basket, and when he saw her he looked surprised. Then he smiled an introduction. "Hi. I'm Gary," he said warmly.

"Lauren. Lauren Maden."

"Great. Are you looking for something? Can I help you?"

Scott moaned from beneath the blankets. "Bowls. She's looking for bowls. But I think my stomach changed its mind. Maybe I'd better wait a little longer before I try to eat anything."

Lauren shrugged, stuck the pot of soup in the refrigerator, and walked past Gary toward Scott. "Okay, well, you know where it's at if you need it. You want me to go now?"

Scott shook his head. "Don't let me breathe on you . . . but stay a few minutes and talk. Tell me what's happening at work."

Lauren pulled a chair closer to the couch. From where they visited, she could see past Scott and on into the bedroom, where Gary had retreated with the basket of laundry. Every few minutes his path crossed the doorway, and she could see him as he placed folded piles of clothes here and there in drawers or in the closet. He emerged a moment later with a stack of bathroom towels. He went straight to the linen closet in the hallway and returned the towels to their place.

He reentered the living room. "I'm making a pot of tea. Anyone else want any?"

Scott muttered, "Some weak tea sounds good."

"What did you say?" Gary asked on his way into the kitchen.

"He said 'weak tea sounds nice,'" Lauren relayed the message. Then she stared as Gary drew mugs from the cupboard and tea bags from the pantry. Gary was strangely at home in Scott's apartment – the same apartment that Lauren had been discouraged from visiting. Obviously Scott's need for privacy didn't extend to this handsome blond stranger.

Lauren's thoughts were interrupted by the shrill whistle of the teakettle. A moment later Gary emerged with a tray and set it on the coffee table in front of Lauren and Scott.

There were three mugs of tea, plus sugar and a little milk There were spoons and a stack of napkins. And then there were cookies. In a bowl.

"I . . . I've got to go now," Lauren suddenly blurted, standing to her feet. "Thanks for the tea, but . . . well, I've got some errands, and I've got to be at work by 3:00 and everything So. . . ."

"Gary, walk Lauren to her car, would you?" Scott gestured from the couch. "I don't think I could make it."

The two walked in silence down the stairs and toward the parking lot. Lauren, her head pounding, walked quickly, saying little and keeping her eyes straight ahead. When they reached her car, Gary held the door open. As she slid into the driver's seat Lauren said simply, "Well, goodbye. Take good care of him·"

Gary locked his eyes onto hers. "I always do."

The tears came somewhere between Colorado and Main. Hot tears that welled up from a place so deep in Lauren's heart that it surprised even her. Her eyes burned and stung as she tried, sobbing, to keep her focus on the road.

She would never be Mrs. Scott Cameron. They would never have little red-haired babies. She would never marry the man she loved; a man who couldn't love her back.

At that point she prayed, a prayer as desperate and as hungry as any she had ever prayed: *God, please change him.*

Gail, wearing an apron and oven mitts, lowered the pot of steaming stuffed cabbage leaves onto a potholder on the formica kitchen table, which had been expanded with the table leaves that, on most days, simply collected dust in the garage. Behind her, the Christmas tree blinked above the vacant inches which had, just that morning, brimmed with colorful packages.

A host of compliments arose from the group of hungry people sitting round the table. Scott's comment was the exception. He said simply, "Smile!" There was a burst of light, and Gail mock-scolded her son as her eyes adjusted from the camera flash. "Lucky for you I didn't startle and drop dinner in your lap."

"Mom, this is my favorite meal. . . . I'd like it any way you served it."

Gail gave Scott a warm squeeze on the shoulder and slipped into her chair. She turned to her husband. "Ready when you are, honey."

Chuck looked around the table at the faces watching him. There was his son-in-law Mitch . . . Tammy, two weeks from her due date . . . Gail . . . Scott . . . and a newcomer named Gary. Scott said the friends had met at the gym or something.

Chuck nodded. "Let's return thanks."

Everyone closed their eyes.

"Blessed Father," Chuck prayed, a sincerity in his voice that evoked a small, curious peek from Scott's friend Gary, "on this Christmas day we remember all the ways You have chosen to reveal Your love to us. The friends and family around this very table are just one of the ways that come to mind. But we also remember the gift of yet another relationship, which began on a starry night in Bethlehem. The gift of Your Son, Jesus, was more than the gift of a baby. It was the present of the relationship that would leave us changed and healed and whole . . . if we let it. Above everything else, our hearts are thankful for that gift tonight and what it has meant in each of our lives. Amen."

Dinner was a mingling of good food, goodwill, warm laughter, and small talk—fodder for fond memories in years to come.

After the table was cleared, the four men retreated to the living room—Chuck to his newspaper and the three younger men to a game of video wars.

Tammy and Gail chatted as they loaded the dishwasher and

set out fresh plates for the lemon cake Gail had baked for dessert. Beyond the green beads at the kitchen window, the December sky was cold and black.

Tammy was counting forks when she mentioned the camera.

"I couldn't believe the Nikon when I saw it. Must have cost a fortune, but I know Scott's thrilled."

Gail finished wiping the water spots off a coffee cup and set it with the others next to the dessert plates. "Oh? Scott bought a new camera?"

"Uh, not exactly. You mean he didn't tell you about it?"

Gail shook her head. Tammy bit her lip and began counting spoons in a hurry. "Oh, he probably just forgot. Mom, the silverware looks great. Did you polish it or something?"

Gail looked absentmindedly into the silverware drawer. "Um, no. I don't think so. What were you saying about a camera?"

"Oh, that was all. Just that he likes it."

For the first time Gail took a good look at the camera Scott had been flashing all evening, laying on the buffet just beyond the kitchen table. It wasn't the old Instamatic. Why hadn't she noticed that before? "Did you say it was a gift? From who?"

"From Gary."

"Oh." Gail set out another coffee cup. A moment later she said, "That's a pretty expensive present, don't you think?"

Tammy shrugged. "Not if you've got money. It's all relative, Mom. Maybe Gary's got a good job."

Tammy left right then to summon the men for coffee and dessert, although she could have done it from where she'd been standing by simply raising her voice the slightest degree.

Over dessert, Gail watched her son with a new eye, seeing small details she'd somehow overlooked before. Small details like the fact that he glowed with happiness. For the first time she noticed the warm interplay between Scott and his new friend, Gary . . . the way they turned to one another for acknowledgment of a witty remark or one-liner. The way they laughed comfortably with each other, as if they'd been friends for a lifetime.

Later, Scott pulled his coat on to leave and came toward Gail for a hug goodbye. She held her son tightly. Before he pulled away, she said, "Come outside with me a minute."

"Now? You'll need a jacket, Mom."

"I'll be fine. This way." Gail led the way out the back door and onto the empty porch. Scott followed.

"Is something wrong, Mom?" he asked, slipping out of his jacket and draping it around Gail's tiny shoulders. "What is it?"

"Nothing, except I wanted to remind you that I love you," Gail said slowly.

"I know that, Mom."

They looked at the stars a few moments. Finally Gail asked, "Scott, is there anything you want to tell me?"

Scott thought a moment. Then he shook his head.

"Okay." Gail said. "Okay. But you know I'll always listen."

"I know, Mom. And thanks."

They went inside then, the secret sensed, but not discovered.

THIRTEEN

Hurtling Toward Destruction

O n New Year's Eve Lauren paced her tiny apartment. She wore a sequined jacket and slacks the color of emeralds, her strawberry-blonde locks piled loosely atop her head. Seductive tendrils played about her face.

Since her heart had been shattered back in November, she and Scott had continued "dating"—or whatever it was they did. Lauren could never seem to gather the nerve to ask Scott directly about . . . *that* issue, although many times in conversation she had opened the door, so to speak, for Scott to tell her he was gay. He never took the opportunity.

Tonight Lauren was taking destiny in her own hands.

There was a knock at the door. Lauren nearly jumped out of her skin.

She slid the deadbolt aside and gestured Scott inside. He looked at her and nodded. "Nice. Very nice. Ready to go? Where's your purse?"

Lauren kneaded her hands together. "I'll get it later. Actually . . . there's no rush. The party doesn't start right away."

Scott's eyes narrowed. "No? When does it start?"

"Not for another hour and a half. Not till seven. I thought . . . I thought we needed to talk."

Scott stiffened. "You lied to me. I can't believe you lied to me."

"We need to talk Scott. *Please* don't put me off again. I

think . . . I think I know why we can't be more than friends, and it's okay."

Scott clenched one fist till his knuckles went white. He threw his car keys on the couch. "You don't know anything, Lauren. Not a thing."

"Maybe I do . . . maybe I don't." Lauren felt a knot of tears well up in her throat. "But I know I love you. I love you, and I need to know where we're going. Is our relationship entirely one sided? Or is there the chance that it could grow . . . that you could grow to love me, too?"

Scott was breathing hard. "You tricked me!" His nostrils flared. "Don't you ever, *ever* trick me like this again. Do you understand me?"

Lauren, her eyes beginning to sting with tears, fumed back: "No! No, I *don't* understand. That's the whole point."

"Look. You want to know if our friendship will grow? Well, I don't have the answer. Right now I just don't know, okay? But I can promise you one thing—you pull this kind of stunt again and it *won't*. Now just don't do anything to ruin the evening, okay? Let's just—I don't know—go get a coke or something until the party starts. Just *don't* ruin the evening."

Lauren snatched her purse from the couch, her mouth pressed into a thin line. She passed Scott on the way toward the door, then suddenly melted and turned, eyes pleading, toward him. "Scott, I'm in *love* with you. What's happening here?" A single tear slipped down a creamy cheek.

Scott let out a sigh, his hardness dissolving with the makeup beneath Lauren's tear. He looked at Lauren, his eyes nearly as pained as hers. "I don't know, Lauren. I just don't know."

Three days later at work, Lauren was suctioning the lungs of a patient when Scott entered the room to check the stats on the ventilator. At the same moment, a young woman technician named Lee walked into the room with a tray and instructions to draw blood from the woman in the bed.

Lee set the tray on the bedside table and proceeded to pre- pare a syringe. As she worked, she smiled up at Scott. "So, Scott. What'd you get Lauren for Christmas? A diamond ring?"

Scott looked like a man who had just been belted in the stomach. He managed a swallow, then shot a fierce look at Lauren, who simply gave a cool shrug. Scott looked back at Lee and forced a laugh. "What? You're kidding, right?"

Lee looked from Scott to Lauren and back to Scott again, sensing the tension and looking for a clue in someone's eyes as to what the story was. In the end, she simply said, "Okaaay," and focused a little too abruptly on her work.

Lauren finished her duties, collected her equipment, and left the room. Scott followed. In the hall, when he knew they were alone, he hissed: "Are you talking to people, Lauren? Everyone thinks we're . . . we're a *thing*."

Lauren whirled to face the man she loved. "What are we, Scott? Maybe if you knew what the heck we actually were, you wouldn't be so paranoid about what other people think." With that she turned and walked away.

Scott stood, stinging, watching her go.

But despite the magnitude of the feelings involved, the fight didn't last long.

Around eight o'clock that evening, Lauren emerged from the break room, holding two aspirins in the palm of one hand and rubbing the back of her neck with the other. She wondered how much of her headache was due to physical reasons and how much was the result of the whole thing with Scott.

Scott caught up with her at the drinking fountain.

"Lauren, look at this." His voice was hedged with fear. He pointed to his forearm, visible beneath a rolled up sleeve, and to a dark bruise the size of a quarter. "I just found this mark. What do you think?"

Lauren looked at the bruise, then looked at Scott. "So? You bumped your arm."

Scott shook his head. "I don't know. Look at it. I don't remember bumping anything."

The tension between them dissolved as Lauren took Scott's arm tenderly in her hands and inspected the bruise more closely. Then she chewed her lip, thinking. "You've been working out at the gym a lot lately, right?"

Scott nodded. "At least a couple times a week."

"Okay, think about it. Is there anything you're doing—any piece of equipment or particular workout—where your arm could be getting bumped?"

Suddenly Scott went limp. He smiled and his relief was nearly tangible. "Of course. The free weights. I hit my arm on the weight stand two nights ago. What a relief. Thanks, Lauren. Thank you."

The two stood talking for a few more moments, and before parting they made arrangements to grab a piece of pie after work the following night, and then to visit L.A.'s famous Farmers Market on the weekend. Yet the question on Lauren's tongue—the question she didn't dare ask—was why a simple bruise had thrown Scott into a tailspin.

She almost asked Scott if he were afraid of getting AIDS. But she didn't. For her, as well as Scott, reality was most comfortable kept at arm's length.

Scott canceled their pie date at the last minute. Lauren was disappointed, but not surprised. It was hardly the first time Scott had flaked out on their plans.

But Saturday proved to be a fun-filled day as Scott and Lauren spent the hours shopping, eating and sightseeing at the colorful Farmers Market. Around three in the afternoon, just before they decided to call it quits and head for home, Scott and Lauren passed a picturesque meat and deli shop. Scott ran in just long enough to buy a present for his parents: a ham.

"Oh man, they're gonna love this." He beamed as they walked back to his Mustang with the ham under his arm.

"Why? What's so special about a ham?" Lauren laughed.

"Not just *any* ham, Lauren. A *Taylor's* ham. You can hardly get them around here. Mostly back East. My folks used to get Taylor's hams when they were newlyweds living in Washington, D.C. It's like an old family tradition."

They got back to Lauren's apartment by 4:00 and called Gail and Chuck from there.

"Mom!" Scott said into the phone as soon as Gail picked up the receiver. "You and Dad gonna be home awhile?"

At the other end of the line, Gail nodded. "Sure, honey. Are you coming over?"

"Yeah. Me and Lauren. We'll come right now."

"Oh?" Gail brightened at the mention of Lauren Maden. She had grown to love Scott's pretty coworker and friend. She could only hope Scott was doing the same. "Did you two do anything special today?"

"We sure did. It was fun. And we've got a surprise for you."

Suddenly Gail stood stock still, as if moving might shatter the illusion. Did she dare hope . . . ? Could it possibly be . . . ?

"Surprise?" she finally said. "Can't you tell me what it is over the phone?"

"No need," Scott answered casually. "We'll be there in fifteen minutes. Bye."

Gail hung up the phone gingerly, not wanting to burst the bubble of hope that glistened in rainbow colors around her. She walked slowly into the bedroom, where Chuck was lying on the bed, resting his joints from the arthritis that plagued them.

"Chuck," Gail said slowly, brimming and beaming as only a mother can. "There's good news. I think Scott and Lauren are engaged."

Scott chattered happily all the way to his parents' home. He had always loved giving: creating small surprises, sending greeting cards for no apparent reason, writing letters, brightening a life wherever and however he could. Lauren simply listened, smiling and shaking her head. All this fuss. Over a *ham*. Ah, but who could know the significance of a family tradition. . . .

Later, the thing that didn't add up was the look on Gail's face as Scott awarded her with the big surprise. Lauren couldn't tell for sure from where she stood in the doorway, just behind Scott. But she thought . . . she was fairly certain . . . that Gail looked like she was ready to cry.

A few days later, on a Friday, Matthew Ross Hadley was born. Along with the rest of the family, Scott had held vigil at the hospital throughout the long hours of labor until the baby was finally delivered a few minutes after noon. He went back the next day to visit his sister and peer at little Matthew again through the nursery window. And that night, he resorted to his faithful pen to try to sort out the emotions running rampant through his heart:

He's so beautiful—actually darling! He looks a lot like Mitch, not too much like Tammy—and he has red hair.

A redhead in the family! The first member of the new generation, and he has red hair!

It was so odd yesterday, as Mom and I watched the baby through the nursery window—just minutes after the delivery. He has quite a temper; he was waving his arms and crying!

I had such a sense of deja-vu. It was like watching myself, twenty-seven years ago. A son. A red-haired son.

And I felt, oddly enough, a sense of relief.

You see, I know that I'll probably never marry or have children of my own. That's so . . . sad. But now that Tammy has a child, well . . . I love that baby, and I'll help take care of him as if he were my own.

More than that though. . . . If something should ever happen to me, and I should die . . . well, the hope and promise of a new baby might just help my family bear the loss.

As the months passed, Scott's life settled into a series of comfortable patterns, despite a few threatening features.

Scott and Lauren continued their friendship, Scott managing to overlook the fact that Lauren was becoming increasingly possessive of his time and increasingly resentful of Gary. The secret that Scott had yet to admit Lauren already knew with her heart, and the knowledge gnawed away inside her like acid.

By then Lauren's most earnest prayer had changed. She was no longer asking God to change Scott Cameron. Instead, she began to plead, *God, change me. If You aren't going to change Scott, do something with me. I don't want to love him. I'm getting hurt. I'm in love with this guy and he can't return it.*

It didn't take long for Gary Anderson to develop his own opinion of Lauren, growing to refer to his rival, without fail, as

"The Pest." Gary had become a permanent fixture around Scott's place; in fact, Scott's handsome lover wanted to move in. While Scott wasn't quite ready for that, he and Gary continued seeing each other on an almost daily basis. Occasionally, the two talked about buying a tiny condo together somewhere on the waterline in Malibu, spending their days enjoying the surf and the sand and the sun.

The fantasy might have grown out of their mutual love for the beach . . . or possibly from a primal longing for something that resembled — as long as they couldn't have the real thing — a settling down of sorts into homelife and family.

But whatever its source, the beachhouse dream was fueled by the harsh realities of the lifestyle they had chosen. In increasing numbers, friends and lovers of friends were being diagnosed with the deadly AIDS virus. Scott knew several men who were dead. Too many others were dying.

The beachhouse fantasy seemed a wonderful escape from the ever-looming specter of death and disease. It also seemed like a nice way to spend the last few months of life on this earth — if it ever came to that.

On Thursday, July third, Scott awoke to a bedroom flooded with dusty sunlight. He stretched lazily, drew the sheet tighter around him and renuzzled his face into his pillow.

Suddenly he bolted upright. He grabbed the clock on the bedtable and jerked it toward him, yanking the chord out of the wall. He read the time and flopped back on the mattress with relief.

He wasn't late.

Fifteen minutes later, Scott was singing in the shower when Gary let himself in the front door with the key Scott had given him. He fixed himself a cup of Earl Grey and browsed through a copy of *Reader's Digest* while Scott finished his shower and dressed quickly. Then the two men, exchanging small talk along the way, went briskly down the outside steps and climbed into the Mustang.

The ride into Hollywood went quickly. On the day before the

Fourth of July, there was already a vacation feel in the air. Traffic was at a minimum. It seemed that half the city had taken Thursday off, giving themselves a four-day weekend and lightening the roads. Or, as Gary joked, the light traffic was simply a good omen. A small favor from the gods.

They arrived at the medical building a few minutes early. Last week, upon entering the elegant foyer, Scott had slowed his pace to admire the slick marble floors and the modern art sculptures in soldered brass that helped create the sterile, sophisticated mood of the place.

But today he and Gary brushed past the $40,000 sculptures and went straight for the elevators, wrapped in dialogue about a movie they'd seen two nights before.

The elevator stopped at the ninth floor. Scott and Gary retraced a maze of corridors before entering a door in the left wing of the building.

Dr. Gibson Thomas was a burly man with the shoulders of a body builder and a head of black wavy hair that only half his clients realized was a toupee. He had established his practice in the early seventies, and now had a steady clientele, many of whom—like Gary—felt strongly about the politics of pumping their "gay" dollars into "gay" business. Dr. Thomas's homosexual lover functioned as the receptionist for the office and took Gary's and Scott's names right away.

The doctor saw Gary first about a small mole Gary wanted removed on the back of his neck near the hairline.

Scott waited in the foyer, reading *Life* magazine, analyzing the pattern of the wallpaper, noting that the paper cup holder mounted to the water cooler was empty. He admired a print on the wall above the cooler: It was a picture of a pair of dilapidated running shoes, and it bore some caption about being worn and tired and old . . . but comfortable. Later that afternoon, the image of the print and its caption about aging would haunt Scott, and he would find black humor in its placement in a waiting room frequented by gay men, most of whom were in their twenties and thirties—all of whom faced the possibility of dying before the end of the decade.

When Gary emerged from the inner sanctuary, his eyes caught Scott's for a fraction of a heartbeat. Then his gaze dropped. He claimed one of the three chairs in the lounge and reached for a magazine, his hand trembling imperceptibly.

Scott stood. "Be right back," he said, heading toward the door and his turn in the exam room. He was going to get the results of some routine tests done on a couple of scabs he'd found on his scalp. Scott was a little nervous, but only because Gary had filled him with horror stories about the heartbreak of psoriasis and some tar-based shampoo treatment that Gary assured would also take the luster out of Scott's locks.

The door closed behind Scott.

Gary threw the magazine back onto the table and glanced down at his watch. For several minutes after that, he counted the multicolored nubs on the arm of his chair. He finally tore his gaze away and locked it onto the examination room door, waiting, wondering, dying a little inside at the news he harbored.

Gary's thoughts were bitter. They'd had eight months together. Eight months. And now it would all crash and grind to a painful, gruesome halt. One thing was sure, Gary thought to himself, the beachhouse idea had just been shot to. . . .

Suddenly the door swung open, snapping Gary from his thoughts. Scott emerged, his face ashen. He looked at Gary, a question in his eyes. Gary nodded, wordless, but the message came through loud and clear. Yes, he'd been told. Gary knew that Scott had Kaposi's Sarcoma, a rare form of cancer. And both men knew what that meant.

Acquired Immune Deficiency Syndrome. . . .

AIDS.

The two exited the office without a word. When they hit the plush carpet in the empty hallway, Scott looked up at Gary and said simply, "What are we going to do?"

Gary never answered.

There simply weren't any words that made any sense at that moment.

The next day was the Fourth of July. Scott managed to put

in a cameo appearance at the family barbecue, less than twenty-four hours after telling Gail and Chuck that he was going to die.

In the late afternoon, shortly after Scott had left, Gail claimed that she'd eaten too much potato salad and needed to stretch her legs. She asked if Tammy wanted to come along, leaving baby Matthew with Chuck and Mitch.

The two women strolled down the quiet residential street, the same street where Tammy had learned to skate and Scott had learned to ride a bike; the street where Chuck had taught Scott to drive; the street on which yellow school buses had once rumbled, collecting and depositing two Cameron kids, one of whom typically had comic books stashed between his texts.

And it was the same street where, just yesterday, Scott had sat in his car and agonized over the fact that he had lived two separate lives . . . until the discovery that he had AIDS derailed public life and private struggle from parallel tracks and sent them crashing together in a blinding, shuddering, smoking mass.

And, as he had sat in his car on that quiet, tree-lined street, postponing the moment he would give his folks the news, Scott had to wonder: Was there anything left in his life to rebuild? Would he ever emerge from the wreckage?

Gail cleared her throat. "Tammy."

Tammy, who had been watching a sparrow fluttering and hopping on the lawn next door, turned to her mother. "Mmm?"

"Scott told us. He told us he's gay."

Tammy's heart skipped a beat. Then she let out a small sigh. She sneaked a sideways glance at her mother. "Are you okay?"

"No. No, I'm not okay." Gail bit her lip. She couldn't say more. The rest of the story had to come from Scott himself. Scott wanted to be the one to tell Tammy about the AIDS.

Tammy shook her head. "I've known for a while, Mom."

"I know. He told us you knew. I'm glad he . . . he at least turned to you."

Tammy continued. "I'm afraid for him. I'm afraid of the consequences. He'll reap destruction somehow—we just don't know how."

At that point Gail broke into sobs.

FOURTEEN

Thank God for Friends

S cott picked up the phone and dialed Lauren's number on Saturday morning. When she answered, he simply said he wouldn't be able to make the lunch they had planned that afternoon.

"Scott Cameron," Lauren pretended to pout, "I'd be ticked at you . . . if I weren't so used to you flaking out on me like this."

Scott promised that he'd see her when their shift started at three. He said there was something he needed to do first.

He grabbed his keys, slamming the front door behind him.

All the way down the stairwell and toward his car, Scott couldn't shake the feeling that he was imprisoned in a giant pendulum, slowly swinging, swaying, back and forth. Every time the throbbing in his soul began to dull, the pendulum swung him back toward terror. Every time he found a few moments' sanctuary—in sleep, in a comic book, in a '40s picture on television, or even in a few too many drinks—the pendulum swung, and he found himself flung back into an emotional war zone, with memories like shrapnel screaming above his head and dead dreams littering the blood-stained ground on which he lay. Every time he allowed himself to believe that if he just closed his eyes tight enough this nightmare would all go away, the pendulum swung again, and he found himself grieving over all the loved ones who would be devastated when he told them the news.

As the pendulum swayed, it seemed to him that the seconds mocked him as they ticked, and that great hands of the clock on which he rode stood poised and erect, just moments away from the stroke of midnight.

Time was running out.

Scott found Tammy at their parents' house and maneuvered her into the spare room where they'd have a few moments of privacy. First Scott mentioned his big scare with hepatitis a few years earlier, and somehow from there eased into the news that he had AIDS. Tammy said she knew it was a gay disease, but didn't know much else about the virus. Scott explained that within five years he would very likely be dead. Tammy stood on tiptoe to give Scott a long hug. She told him not to worry. She said that five years was a long time; she was *sure* someone would come up with a cure by then.

Several hours later, Scott negotiated into a tight space in the parking lot at St. Luke's. For just a few priceless moments, Scott found himself distracted by the rote mechanics of parking, locking his car, and sprinting across the parking lot. He felt himself merge into the fast-paced scurry of the hospital environment, welcoming the merging because it left less space for the hurricane of emotions.

He ran into Lauren nearly at once. She was talking to the family of one of the new patients, a woman who'd nearly died when her boyfriend tried to race a train at a crossing. The man was killed instantly; his girlfriend would live but with more than a few scars. Scott waited on the sidelines for Lauren's conversation to end. He watched the faces of the family, feeling just a little of their pain. Scott knew what it felt like to race out of control. And Scott knew what it felt like to lose.

Lauren broke away from the huddle of people. She turned, catching Scott in the first sweep of her eyes. Her face brightened.

But Scott's heart beat in shadows. The pendulum had swung again. Reality was a harsh master.

"Scott! I've been looking for you!" Lauren gushed.

"Got any plans tonight?" He got right down to business.

Lauren shook her head.

"Then we've got to do something. Can you come over after work?"

"You mean to *your* place?"

"Yeah."

Lauren studied Scott with her eyes. "Okay. Sure."

He turned to leave then, although Lauren watched until he rounded the corner and disappeared out of sight. She just couldn't figure it.

By 11:30 that night they were alone in Scott's apartment, sitting side by side on the couch. Lauren's hands were clammy with a nervous sweat. Scott offered refreshments a few too many times.

Suddenly Lauren giggled. "Did I tell you my uncle's in town?"

"No," he hedged, shooting her a sideways glance.

She giggled again. "He's a mental case. I'm not joking. We kids used to call him Candy Bar behind his back because he's half nuts, you know. He's staying with my folks, and you should hear the horror stories. I mean, two days ago he baked cookies with cat food in them."

Lauren laughed a little too hard. Scott didn't laugh at all. Lauren flew into another story, her words tumbling over themselves in a nervous rush.

Suddenly Scott lay down, resting his head in her lap.

Lauren shut up, staring down wide-eyed at the man she loved, his cheek against her thighs. She reached out a hand, tentatively. He didn't move. She touched his hair. He never said a word. Her hand smoothed his hair . . . touched his face. He lay there, absorbing her touch, not moving a muscle.

She pulled her hand away.

"Scott," she said quietly. "What's wrong?"

He sat up then, and there were tears in his eyes. "You wrote something in a card once—I think it was for my birthday. You promised me that there was nothing I could say or do that would make you stop loving me. Do you remember?"

Lauren nodded, fear mushrooming up inside her.

"I'm going to hold you to that promise," Scott said in a hoarse voice.

Lauren nodded again. Now she was beginning to feel numb.

"I went to the doctor. I had a lump. I had it removed. . . And it was Kaposi's Sarcoma."

Lauren's heart shattered and crumpled into tiny fragments. She reached out then, folding Scott into her arms. She held him for a moment, and then he freed his arms enough to wrap them tightly around her shoulders. They held each other like that, but it wasn't long enough. It could never be long enough.

Scott broke the silence. "Do you understand what I'm telling you?" he asked, his words muffled, his face still buried in her strawberry hair.

Lauren wanted to snap, *What do you think I am? An idiot? You're gay. You've got AIDS. . . .* She wanted to scream, to fling words at him, to batter him with the knowledge he'd given her—knowledge that was far too terrible to contain in silence.

But in the end she just said "yes" and wrapped herself tighter around his waist—as the clock on the bookshelf marked the passing of the seconds like heartbeats.

The next day Gail packed a small bag of belongings and drove to her grandmother's home two cities away. Grandma Rose was nearing ninety and as fragile as a wisp of warm breath on winter air.

Gail had already decided that Grandma Rose should never know the truth about Scott. When the time came, the family would tell her that her great-grandson was dying of cancer. Nothing more. But it was too soon for even that.

Gail thought that Scott's grandmother—Gail's mother and Grandma Rose's daughter—should know the truth. But Lisbeth Perkins was out of town for a few days; she wouldn't be home until Wednesday.

Until then, Gail needed to sense her heritage, to draw close to the strength of generations, even if that strength was to be found only in the frail form of a woman half-senile with age. And so she had called Grandma Rose and invited herself over for a couple days' visit. The old woman had been delighted.

Sunday afternoon, Grandma Rose sat in her favorite chair, in the sunny spot beneath the living room window, and read the *Sunday Times* with a shaky eye and a shakier hand. She put down the paper and looked at Gail, who was doing needle-point as she sat on the blue divan with the lace doilies on the armrests.

"Gail, honey, what's this AIDS all about?"

Gail jumped.

Grandma Rose shook the newspaper in her hand. "There's AIDS on every page nowadays. It seems this Rock Hudson fella has it, and everybody's gone a goo-goo over it all. Such a big to-do!"

"Well, Grandma," Gail said slowly, "it's a disease that kills off a person's immune system, so their body sort of welcomes in whatever ailments are out there in the air. Colds, flu, infec-tions . . . even more serious diseases like cancer. And it's fatal, Grandma. They think that once you get the disease, it's just a matter of time until you die."

Grandma Rose shook her head, sitting quietly in the patch of warm sunlight. "Those poor, poor people," she muttered. After a few minutes she lifted the newspaper and went on to the next article.

But Gail was still sitting quietly, her needlepoint forgotten in her lap.

Two days later, Gail kissed her grandmother goodbye and headed home. On the way, she took a small detour and pulled into the parking lot of a Christian bookstore.

She browsed the aisles, looking for something—something specific.

"Can I help you?" an Asian woman with a warm smile and cross-shaped earrings approached Gail.

"I'll . . . I'll just browse a few minutes more," Gail waved off the clerk.

Twenty minutes later, Gail found what she was searching

for: a book by a woman named Barbara Johnson.[1] Years ago, Gail had heard Barbara speak at a women's luncheon. Barbara had a gay son, and she spoke firsthand of the betrayal, the hurt, the embarrassment—and the healing—that her family had experienced. At that time, Gail had listened politely, thinking, *Thank God this doesn't apply to me.*

But now she paid for the book quickly and, clutching the package the way a dying man might hold a life preserver, hurried out to her car.

In the coming days, Scott told Lauren things about his life that he had hoped she would never have to know. He told her that most of the times he had flaked out on a date, he did so to spend the time with Gary. He told her he and Gary had been lovers since last September. He said Lauren and Gary were a little alike—they both wanted more of a romantic commitment than Scott felt he could give.

Then one night he showed her the journals.

Lauren stared in awe at the crowded box pulled from beneath the bed.

"Why?" she finally asked.

Scott looked thoughtful. "There's something about self-disclosure. I think I crave total honesty, the ability to just open up and pour myself out."

"But in a diary?"

Scott shrugged. "I let loose my thoughts—examine and explore them. There was no one else, Lauren . . no one else to share my thoughts with. I think it's been important for me to share them with myself."

Lauren peered at Scott. "No one else? I think there could have been, Scott."

"Maybe, maybe not." Scott began replacing the journals in the box. He slid it back under the bed. "I find it interesting that the people who have reacted with the most venom to the news that I'm gay have been the same people who claim to be representatives of God's love."

Lauren, sitting crosslegged on the bedroom floor, tossed Scott a challenge. "Like who?"

"Tony . . . Tony Lozano and Kirk Graham, for starters."

Lauren smiled. "Scott, I don't know about this Kirk guy, but Tony seems to be sticking closer than a brother. And you say he knows you're gay?"

Scott nodded.

"It sounds to me like you're lumping Christians all together in the same boat—just like some people lump gays all together. But I don't think it's that cut and dried."

"No?"

Lauren shook her head. "I'm still around. And look at your parents—they couldn't be more supportive. And Tammy loves you dearly. We don't . . ." she struggled with the words. "We can't accept your lifestyle—I don't, anyway. It's destroying you, Scott. It's wrong, and it's destroying you. But we still love *you*. I know I still love you."

The two fell silent a moment.

Finally Lauren added, "You fought the war for a long time . . alone. You kept losing the battles, and so you surrendered. But maybe, if you had opened up sooner, if you would have been honest about your struggles at the time—maybe things would be different now."

"Maybe. Maybe I shouldn't have. . . ."

Just then the front door opened and Gary's voice rang out: "Scott, it's me-eee."

Lauren froze.

Scott gave her hand a warm squeeze. "Don't freak out. It's just Gary."

"I *know* who it is," Lauren hissed.

Scott lowered his voice. "I know you hate him. But don't. Please. Wrong or right, he still means a lot. . . ."

"There you are!" Gary spoke from the doorway. Then he saw Lauren and his tone cooled ten degrees. "Oh. Hello, Lauren."

Lauren returned the greeting in a polite—but strained—tone. After several minutes of forced small talk, Lauren announced she had to leave. Scott saw her to the door. She said goodbye, then smarted inside as the door closed behind her and Scott turned back to his other guest.

I know why I don't like Gary; but what does he have against me? Lauren wondered as she drove away. *After all, he's the victor; he won the prize. Scott chose Gary over me.*

Toward the end of July, Scott applied for disability and left his job at the hospital. He wasn't a danger to the patients; but the patients at St. Luke's, with their varied and sometimes fatal diseases, posed a serious health risk to Scott.

Still, the forced time off presented an adjustment. Scott had to think of new ways to fill his time. He continued his journalism classes at City College. He continued working out at the gym and tanning himself at the beach. By now Scott looked as fit as he ever had, with strong browned shoulders and sun-lightened hair. When he looked in the mirror, he was pleased. But he couldn't help wondering what he would see six months from now. . . .

Some afternoons Scott drove to his parents' home, and chatted with Gail when she got home from school. One afternoon, he was sitting at the kitchen table with a glass of milk and a bag of Pecan Sandies when he noticed a large shipping envelope on the buffet. The envelope was open, spilling an avalanche of cassette tapes.

Wandering to the buffet, Scott picked up a tape. Its label read "Spatula Ministries." Scott turned to Gail, who was slicing onions in the kitchen for a pot of chili she was making.

"What's all this, Mom?"

Gail looked up, careful not to slice her finger as she did. "Oh, that. Some tapes this woman sent me."

"I can see they're tapes. What kind of tapes?" Scott replaced the cassette on the pile and returned to his cookies.

"Have you ever heard of a woman named Barbara Johnson?" Scott shook his head no.

"Well, she wrote this book about her family. Her son is . . her son is gay." Gail watched Scott's face for his reaction. There wasn't any. "Anyway, she has this ministry now, called Spatula, for parents of gay children."

"Spatula," Scott repeated. "Why Spatula?"

Gail gave a nervous laugh. "Well, she says when parents first find out their kids are gay, they need someone to come along with a spatula and scrape them off the ceiling."

There was an awkward silence.

"Mom . . . I'm sorry."

"I know, Scott. I know you are." She put the knife down and walked around the counter toward her son.

"Dad's taking it hard, isn't he?" Scott sighed.

Gail nodded, pulling up a chair beside Scott. "I can hardly get him to talk about it. Whenever he does, he just starts crying." There was a pause. "Scott," she said suddenly, drawing her son's attention. "Maybe God will heal you. I'm praying that He will."

"I'm praying, too, Mom."

"If He does . . ." Gail leaned toward Scott, as if she were about to share a great secret, or receive one, "if we all get through this, can it end? Can you leave the . . . the lifestyle?"

Scott's lips moved in a hint of a smile. "Oh, Mom. If only it were that simple."

"Well? Lauren's a beautiful girl. And she loves you, Scott."

"I know she does. But Mom, let me ask you something. Could you suddenly become gay? Could you . . . could you love another woman?"

Gail recoiled. Her face registered her shock. "Of course not! That's the most ridiculous thing I've ever heard!"

"Mom, it's like that for me. I wish everyone could under- stand," Scott blurted. "Even now, knowing I'm probably going to die and knowing I made some awful choices that got me where I am today, life isn't perfect. Everything doesn't 'fall into place' just because I want it to badly enough. There aren't any easy answers. I still love Gary, you know."

"I . . . I wondered," Gail said tentatively.

"I wish I could say that knowing I'm dying somehow ripped all the old desires out of my heart and soul for good. But life isn't that perfect."

"No," Gail agreed, speaking softly, almost to herself, "I guess it's not."

Scott gushed on, intoxicated with the new feeling of communicating himself—all of himself, the good and the bad. "Somehow, something got twisted up inside me. I don't understand it All I know is that I've struggled for a long time. And even before I knew exactly what the struggle was, before I could quite define it, I knew I was different from the other kids. Even when I was little, Mom. I knew I was different."

Gail stared at her son, seeing a stranger sitting there. Even his features seemed unfamiliar. Then she shook her head, and the illusion scattered. When she looked back again, she saw Scott watching her. She sighed. "Maybe it's because you were sickly as a little boy. Maybe that had something to do with it."

Scott recalled the years he couldn't play rough like the other boys, because a rare digestive disorder—coupled with asthma—had left him weak and vulnerable to injuries and illness He shrugged. "Maybe."

"Well, I don't understand any of this." Gail shook herself up from the table, remembering the chili bubbling away on the stove without any onions. "But maybe I'll understand more when I meet with Barbara Johnson."

Scott looked as if he'd been slapped. "Barbara Johnson? The tape lady? You're meeting with her? Why?"

Gail looked surprised at Scott's reaction. "Why? Because I'm going crazy here, trying to deal with all this. Your father can't talk about it; you're going through enough without me unloading all my fears on you. I need someone I can turn to. You didn't expect me to face this all alone, did you?"

"I guess not," Scott muttered.

Gail reclaimed the knife, the onion crunching as she sliced off another chunk. "Thank God for friends" was all she said.

NOTE

1. Barbara Johnson, *Where Does a Mother Go to Resign?* (Minneapolis, MN: Bethany House Publishers, 1979).

FIFTEEN

Emerging
from the Wreckage

S cott stopped to catch his breath after the third flight of stairs in the library at Long Beach State University. He leaned against the railing, wiped perspiration from his brow and blew out a gale of air from his lungs. Students carrying bookbags and umbrellas ambled down the steps, laughing with classmates or nodding heads in rhythm to the beat from their Walkmans. They flooded around Scott and Tony, who stood at the hairpin turn between one flight of stairs and the next.

"Next time we'll take the elevator," Scott said, still gasping for air. With a free hand he pulled up drooping, baggy pants.

"You okay?" Tony reached out and gripped Scott's shoulder firmly.

"Yeah. I get winded easily these days," Scott said with a mixture of embarrassment and self-recrimination. "Just one more flight of stairs."

On the fourth floor, Scott and Tony stopped to rest and look out a bank of picture windows at the dark November sky. Angry clouds showered rain like a celestial sprinkler system at full blast. Scott watched as a woman ran toward the library with a limp, sopping newspaper held overhead. Other students and professors milled in the lobby, zipping jackets, popping umbrellas, and mustering their courage before launching into the sheets of rain.

Soon Scott and Tony stalked through catacombs of towering bookshelves. Rows upon rows of musty, dusty volumes stretched before them. Scott boomed out a crashing cough that sent an echo ricocheting through the stacks.

"You all right?" Tony asked.

"Yeah," Scott assured, slapping his chest as if to punish it for hacking. He checked the slip of paper in his hand, looked at the index card on the side of the shelf next to him, and walked on. A few more rows and he stopped. "Okay. This should be the one."

The two shimmied down the narrow aisle and crouched before a stack of bound magazines. They squinted at the tiny, typewritten numbers and letters on the spines of the books.

"There it is—*New England Journal of Medicine*," Tony pointed. "Which month did you need?" He handed Scott two stacks of journals from the previous year. Scott checked his paper again and began thumbing through the pages.

"Yeah, here it is: 'HIV and Kaposi's Sarcoma: A Deleterious Link.'"

"Delet-what?" Tony repeated.

"Deleterious. I think it means harmful."

"Oh. Sorry I asked."

Scott struggled to his feet, the volumes beneath his arm. "Now let's get those back issues of *Southern Medical Journal* and then head downstairs to look at the current issues."

Two hours later, Tony and Scott sat in the campus coffee shop, leaning over Styrofoam cups of steamy coffee. Their jackets were draped over the backs of their chairs, and a damp umbrella gave up its last pools of moisture at Tony's feet. On the table, next to Scott's elbow, sat a Manila folder bulging with Xeroxed copies of medical reports and journal articles.

". . . and then I got this notice about my insurance premiums," Scott was saying. "St. Luke's said since I'm not a paid employee—I'm on disability, you know—that they can't continue paying my insurance premiums."

"Is it a lot?"

"One sixty a month . . . but that's a chunk compared to the nineteen I was paying." Scott tore open a packet of sugar and dumped it in his coffee. "But figure this. I get only six hundred a month on disability, and my rent's four hundred right off the bat. Take away another one sixty . . . that's gonna leave me forty bucks a month for food, gas, clothes, car repairs, whatever."

"All your medical expenses are covered, right?"

Scott shook his head. "Just the first eighty percent."

"Whoa, Scott," Tony winced. "What are you going to do?"

"I have no idea. I may have to move out of my apartment, maybe move home. But I hate that idea. This whole thing's already a huge emotional burden on my folks—I don't want it to be a financial burden as well."

Tony furrowed his brows in thought. "I wish there was something I could do to help. . . ."

Scott waved off the offer. "Just you being here with me is a big help. Just the friendship, you know?" Suddenly Scott looked at Tony, his eyes narrowing. "Speaking of 'friendship,' do Kirk or Joel know I have AIDS? It's been four months now. I would have thought the world knew by now."

Tony looked embarrassed. "Yeah. I think they know."

Scott snorted with disgust. "Well, thanks for the compassion,'" he said sarcastically to one in particular.

Tony fiddled with the flip top on the stainless steel creamer "Hey, they just don't know what to say, you know?"

"Anything would be better than ignoring me altogether."

Tony stared at the creamer, avoiding Scott's eyes. "You need to know. Joel took it pretty hard. I mean about you being gay. He felt . . . well, he felt pretty betrayed."

"Betrayed?" Scott's voice rose a pitch. "I'll tell you who was betrayed. They betrayed *me*, Tony. I used to think we were close.'"

Tony locked his eyes onto Scott's. "That's exactly what Joel said."

Scott swallowed his next words. He looked at Tony and finally asked, "What did he mean?"

"He said you lied to him. Not with your words, I guess, since you guys never exactly discussed you being gay or anything. But you lied with your life."

"That's a cop out."

Tony shrugged. "Joel said he must've asked you a dozen times or more what was happening in your life. And not just the shallow 'How are you doing?' stuff that everyone asks everyone and nobody ever means. He said he really tried. He said you put on a good facade."

Scott didn't respond. His jaw was set in a stubborn line and he stared sullenly into his coffee. Maybe Joel was right . . . maybe Scott had betrayed them all by laughing on the outside and crying on the inside. But he'd never thought of it that way. All those years of silent suffering, he thought the only one who was getting hurt was Scott Cameron.

"It's hard to say, Tony. It's hard to say exactly what went . . ." Scott's sentence was cut short by a hacking cough that rocketed unexpectedly from his lungs. He turned away from the table, doubling over, and hacked again into his fist. He stopped for a moment and pounded at his chest with one fist.

It was the kind of gravely, wet cough that drew the attention of the other patrons. A few people craned their neck to see who was sick enough to cough like that. Scott had fought off a lot of bugs in his days, but he couldn't seem to shake whatever had latched onto him in the past month or so. He'd lost thirteen pounds and his skin had become blotchy and clammy.

"Maybe we should go, huh, Scott?" Tony suggested, his dark eyes pools of concern.

"Yeah, it's pretty cold in here anyway."

As the two left, a few curious students let their eyes linger on Scott's pallid complexion and gangly body. Scott felt the weight of their stares and, self-conscious, he averted his eyes, looking at the floor as he walked past the other tables. With the manila folder in one hand, he hitched up his pants with the other, then pushed open the glass door with his shoulder.

Two weeks later, shortly after Scott's twenty-ninth birthday, he lay in bed writing in his journal. On that dreary Monday morning in late November, his school textbooks lay scattered on the blanket beside him, and next to his books sat a box of Kleenex. Although it was just two weeks before final exams in Scott's journalism classes, still another cold had forced him to stay indoors.

He took a drink of hot lemon tea and struggled to his feet. He peered out his second story window and pulled the belt of his bathrobe tighter, glad to be inside on such a blustery day. He watched as three children in yellow raincoats and hoods stomped in puddles and raced leaf-boats in the overflowing gutter. They shook a small tree and made a mini-cloudburst rain down on their heads. Scott watched as they convulsed in laughter. Soon a school bus roared to the curb, creating heavy swells in the gutter. The children piled in.

Scott smiled, remembering a small, red-haired boy playing in the rain in front of his parents' house. It was the first and last incident of its kind, since Scott's childhood frailties had left him vulnerable to colds at the slightest chill. But there had been that one afternoon when the rain was light, and Scott had begged to go outside and stomp puddles with his neighborhood friends. Gail denied the request at first, but after Scott had given up, the memory of his pleas changed her mind. "Get your raincoat!" she finally hollered into the bedroom where her seven-year-old had retreated to his books. "And double up your socks. And *try* to stay dry!"

It was useless advice, of course, because an hour later Scott came through the front door soaked to the skin and beaming like a lightbulb. He fell sick that very night with a 103 degree temperature and had congestion in his lungs for weeks. Gail had scolded herself for giving in to such a foolish request. But years later, she admitted to Scott that she would always cherish the memory of standing at the kitchen window, watching Scott's glee as he chased leaves and tasted raindrops and sailed leaf-boats in the swollen gutter.

Warm from the memory, Scott returned to his bed and his books and his journals.

Around four o'clock that afternoon, Scott put down the book he held and cocked his head, listening. He heard the jingle of keys and his apartment door creaking wide. He tried to stand up too quickly and felt his head throb.

"It's just me, Scott," Gary called from the other room. Scott could hear him set down a box, or maybe a bag, and then peel off his jacket. "I brought you some leftover split pea soup from my place," Gary hollered. "You feeling any better?"

Scott shuffled toward the kitchen in his green-and-white striped bathrobe and white sweat socks. His unwashed hair stuck up like a coxcomb in back and his eyes drooped slightly. He carried a crumbled Kleenex in one hand and an empty mug in the other. "'Fraid I don't look like much," Scott announced in a nasally voice. "Soup sounds great. A body can survive only so long on cough drops and lemon tea."

"You're not feeling much better, I take it," Gary said, emptying a small grocery bag.

"I called Dr. Forrester's office and made an appointment for tomorrow."

"God, Scott. You wouldn't have to go through all this if you'd just take better care of yourself. Take your vitamins. Don't skimp on your sleep. And for crissake, go to the doctor when you feel something coming on, not after you're practically too ill to dial the phone."

"Gary, I've read up on this thing. Nothing's going to stop it."

"No. But maybe you can slow it down."

"You know," Scott said, suddenly solemn, "I have a friend who's there already."

"Yeah? Where?" Gary asked, turning up the gas flame beneath the saucepan containing the leftover soup.

"In Heaven."

"Scott, knock it off. Maybe it's not going to come to that. Maybe they'll . . . maybe they'll discover something and. . . ."

"Gary, stop. I've spent my whole life running from reality. I've got to face this one head on."

"You've stopped hoping," Gary snapped. "That'll kill you quicker than anything."

Scott shook his head. "No, I haven't. I still hope. But I'm not as afraid of the alternative as I thought I would be."

"Look. There's this healer I know. She uses crystals. . . ."

"There's no power in that. At least not the right kind. And I'm telling you, Gary. I'm not afraid. Oh yeah, a little, sure. But just a little. I mean, think about it. . . ."

"No thanks."

". . . think about what it would mean to be free of this body, with its pain and imperfections . . . to be forever rid of hatred, evil, and worry . . . to be in the company of the saints, both familiar and those I've only read about . . . to be in the ever-lasting presence of Jesus, and know His perfect love without any restrictions. . . ."

"Mind if we change the subject here? This death-stuff gives me the creeps."

Gary feigned concentration on the bubbling green soup. When he looked up, he caught the image of his reflection in the window. Just to the left, he could see Scott's reflection: gaunt, pale, unkempt. Though Gary wouldn't admit it—to Scott or to himself—he, too, had grave, deep-seated fears. Fears of watching Scott die. Fears for his own health. Fears of losing someone he loved. The fleeting glimpse in the window revealed the stark contrast between the two men.

And the image was a sobering one.

Each week Lauren arrived at Scott's to drive him into Orange County for chemotherapy to combat the Kaposi's Sarcoma. Sometimes she ran into Gary; other times she didn't. Yet even when their paths crossed, the tension between them was beginning to subside. Despite their great differences, Lauren and Gary had one thing in common: They were both in love with the same man, and he was dying.

One Friday after chemo, Scott asked Lauren to drop him off at his parents' rather than back at his apartment. Lauren pulled up at the curb fronting the house, and when Scott reached the porch, she waved and drove off toward home.

Inside, Scott found Gail poring over a stack of letters and papers. Holding his backpack in one hand, he sat down beside his mother on the couch and lifted one of the sheets from the coffee table.

"What's all this?"

"Photocopies of letters from other moms, past issues of their newsletter. . . ." Gail said, lowering the hand that held a hot-pink newsletter.

Scott saw the Spatula logo at the top of the page. "She doesn't miss a week, does she? I mean with the phone calls."

Gail nodded, gratitude glowing in her eyes. "Barbara's steady, that's for sure. Phone calls, care packages, photocopies of letters. . . . Look, Scott," Gail scooped something up from the couch. "I wanted you to see this one. It's from a young man in Ohio who's struggling with homosexuality."

"Oh yeah? What does he say?"

"I think he could use a friend."

Scott reached for the letter. "Were you thinking of me?"

Gail nodded.

Scott shrugged. "I guess I could write him. What's his name?"

"Duane."

"Duane," Scott repeated, thinking. "But Mom, the thing is, I've been there, but I don't have a whole lot of answers for the kid. I don't exactly have six easy steps to crisis-free living, you know."

"Offer what you have, Scott. Not what you don't have."

"What does Barbara Johnson have to offer? What answers does she have? Her son's still gay, isn't he? She's probably still hurting, herself."

"Sure. Which is all the more reason we need each other, Scott."

"But what answers does she have?" Scott pursued.

"Answers . . . God knows, I've begged for them," Gail mused. "I'm beginning to think sometimes there are no answers. I'm beginning to think sometimes there's only grief . . . and comfort. I think some answers will have to wait till we're in Heaven, asking Jesus face to face why we encountered the things we did."

Scott sighed. "Easier said than done."

"I'm not saying we shouldn't look for solutions," Gail was quick to add. "But we can't wait until all the pieces fall into place before we reach out to help . . . or reach out *for* help."

"Like I tried to do." Scott dropped his backpack on the floor. It landed with a thud. "I waited too long, Mom." Scott slumped back on the couch cushions. He paused a moment. "Mom?"

"Mmmm?"

"I've been thinking . . . about my life. About what would happen if God did a miracle and this thing doesn't kill me. I don't think I'll ever be totally free from the homosexual desires. But I've got something now that I never had before—you and Dad and Tammy beside me, Tony and Caroline Lozano, and Lauren. . . . And I've been thinking about Lauren."

"Yes?"

"Maybe if I live, we could have some sort of relationship. I mean more than just friends. It wouldn't be easy. I have a feeling I'd be fighting the old temptations for a long time. But maybe it's enough to take one day at a time, trusting God for the answers to the trials of that single day. Anyway, it's something to think about."

After dinner, Chuck drove Scott back to his apartment. The two men talked about Scott's classes and Tammy's baby and the weather and the Rams. When Scott got out of the car, Chuck leaned across the seat and looked up at his son, standing by the open car door. "Son, do you need anything? Do you need any money?"

Scott smiled and shook his head.

"You know everything I've got is yours, Scotty," Chuck said.

"I know, Dad."

Scott hurried inside so the chill November night wouldn't seep into his bones.

Inside his apartment, he popped open a Pepsi, browsed through the junk mail, put away the clean dishes he'd left drip-drying in a basket in the sink. All the while, his thoughts were with his parents and the newfound closeness he felt whenever they were together. . . .

Scott suddenly put down the second-to-last dish and walked into his bedroom. He opened his desk drawer and rummaged there, withdrawing a small hardbound book with a picture of a blue sky and white clouds imprinted on the cover.

Scott sat at his desk and opened the book. All the pages inside were blank.

He began to write:

Dear Mom and Dad,

A friend gave me this journal a couple weeks ago for my birthday. I think it's really special, so I wanted to put it to a very special use.

So, I decided to make this book a love letter to you both, sharing some of my thoughts and experiences with you each day.

I spent so much of my life isolated from you, an intimate stranger. It's such a joy to be able to talk with you and share myself with you openly — no more secrets or fear, just mutual love and trust.

Do you realize how much that means to me?

Despite everything, I'm so grateful for the way things have turned out, because I've never felt so loved by you, or loved you both so much.

So . . . as I start my twenty-ninth year, allow me to share myself with you.

A week later Scott sank into a lumpy brown chair, clutching a small box of Kleenex. As small talk hummed about the room, his eyes scanned the dozen or so men who formed the ragged half-circle around him. A man named Charles nodded at Scott from across the room, then approached to claim a seat next to Scott Charles, a stocky man with smiling eyes, a crop of black hair, and an even blacker moustache, flashed Scott a "thumbs up."

It was Scott's Thursday night AIDS support group.

The men around him represented varying degrees and pro gressions of their diseases. Some looked healthy by all appearances, even though they, too, had tested HIV-positive, meaning their bodies carried the deadly AIDS virus. Others wore the unmistakable marks of ravaged immune systems, their bodies slowly succumbing to the diseases against which they had no defense. Scott's eyes roamed over withered bodies, spindly limbs sunken eyes, purple lesions, ashen complexions, wispy tufts of hair.

Scott's visual roll-call had become a weekly ritual—to see who was there and, more importantly, who was not.

"I've been depressed all week," one man in the corner looked down at his folded hands as he spoke. He was skinny and pale, but otherwise looked reasonably healthy. "I get fatigued by the simplest tasks. I sleep so much . . . and I feel like I'm just shrinking, shrinking away. Someday I'll just shrink away to nothing. But the depression—that's worse than the physical symptoms. Some days I just can't drag myself out of bed."

All around the room heads nodded. Another man added his comments about his own depression, about visits to the doctor, about a crumbling relationship.

From across the room, a man named Jeff began to speak. Darkness encircled lifeless eyes. Strings of hair did little to cover his flaky, festered scalp. Purple, crusty lesions—Kaposi's Sarcoma—checkered his face and arms. His bones seemed to protrude at every joint, threatening to pierce through papery skin.

Full-blown AIDS. The final stage.

"I've thought more and more about suicide," he said in a guttural voice that seemed to emanate from a dark pit within. "I know I say that every week, but it's beginning to seem like a serious option."

As Scott listened to Jeff, he wondered what lay ahead in his own near future. To see the spectrum of manifestations all in one room was overwhelming. Scott wondered, *Where do I fit on the continuum?* He shuddered to think that he might someday look like Jeff or others in the advanced stages. He snuck glances around the room and groaned inwardly, *Oh God. Oh my God.*

"The worst part is the people who treat you like a leper," Jeff was saying. "They act like if I look at them, they'll get it and die If only they realized they were more dangerous to me than I am to them. At this stage, I'm hardly going to donate blood or lure anyone to my bed; no one's going to catch anything from me. But I could die from a cold I get from them."

Jeff closed his eyes, as though the effort of talking was

exhausting. "Everything is gone," he continued. "Everything I held dear is gone. I can barely feed myself." He began to cry, and those sitting around him reached to embrace him.

Scott, sitting across the room, just stared, the thoughts screaming inside his skull like a drill bit against metal: *I feel like I'm finally learning to live. I don't know how to die. . . .*

Christmas music piped through the crowded mall. Scott, Lauren, and Gary brushed past other shoppers and made their way through the mall, window shopping, browsing in crowded store aisles, admiring winter sweaters on the mannequins in the displays. They stopped once for cups of hot wassail and cinnamon buns, the mid-afternoon winter sun filtering through skylights overhead. Later, the three came to the hub of the mall and looked down from the second floor of shops, onto a open courtyard jammed with people. They leaned over the railing and watched as children, some delighted and some terrified, took their turns on Santa's lap.

"You guys remember doing that?" Lauren asked.

Scott nodded.

Gary, his elbows on the railing, added, "I remember asking him for a wagon. A red wagon."

"Sometimes I wish I could go backwards," Lauren said wistfully. "Back to the days when I was young and the world was magic and even Santa was real. I asked him for a swimming pool one year."

"I'll bet he told you it wouldn't fit in his toy bag," Gary laughed.

Lauren lifted one shoulder and smiled.

"So if the world were still magic and even Santa were real," Gary proposed, "what would you ask him for this year?"

Lauren just shook her head, a small sadness in her voice. "I'm afraid he couldn't give me that either."

Scott's eyes never left the holiday scene below them. Still, he smiled and swayed to bump Lauren's shoulder with his own. "You're right. Not even Santa could fit Harrison Ford in his toy bag."

Lauren squealed. "I don't have a thing for him! What makes you think I have a thing for Harrison Ford?"

"How many times have you seen *Return of the Jedi*?" Scott demanded, tongue-in-cheek. "It's gotta be either Harrison or Chewbacca."

Gary laughed warmly. Lauren smiled, and then she, too, began to laugh.

No one denied that the season seemed tainted by the ominous thoughts hovering in everyone's mind. But that day, the dark cloud seemed to recede just a little.

Especially for Scott. Because Scott felt whole.

Not perfect, mind you. . . .

But whole. For the first time in his life, he was facing his struggles as one person, not as two. He was being honest about his imperfections, honest about his lack of answers, and honest about his quest to find a way to live holy despite his frequent failings.

At least on that single front Scott's future—even if it was a short one—seemed almost bright.

Scott was still basking in that brightness on Thursday as he picked out a card at Hallmark, signed it, and drove the distance to St. Luke's. In one hour, he would take the elevator to the Community Relations wing on the fourth floor to meet with his AIDS support group. But first he had an errand to run. He hurried to catch the elevator, skipping between closing doors and standing in front of two nuns. He pushed the button for the second floor, noticing that they had already pushed the button marked six. He wondered, as people always do, if he were being silently condemned for not taking the stairs for a single floor.

The elevator hummed to a stop. A few minutes later he passed the nurses' station, tossed a wave, and continued toward the east wing, whistling as he went.

One of the nurses, a petite fireball named Lucille, sat at the phone, watching him. Suddenly something dawned on her. "Scott!" she called his name, but he was too far to hear. "Scott!" she yelled again, pushing her chair from the desk to follow him.

A moment later Lucille was hurrying down the corridor

When she came to an intersection she hung a hurried left. She found Scott standing at the open door to one of the rooms. Lucille fell in behind him as he stared, unbelieving, into an empty room where even the bed was stripped naked.

"Scott," Lucille touched his arm. "He died this morning. I tried to catch you but I couldn't."

Scott's voice was hoarse. "No one told me. No one told me he even took a turn for the worse."

"Actually, last night his condition seemed improved. His family hoped it meant something. But then he just went in his sleep."

"Poor Jeff. Then again, he's probably better off," Scott managed. "There were so many things wrong with him. . . ."

Lucille nodded sympathetically, her eyes still fixed on the vacant bed. "Without an immune system, the body's open to so many things. . . . I heard someone last week say that dying of AIDS is like dying a thousand deaths." She caught her breath, then squeezed her eyes closed. "Whoops. Sorry, Scott. . . ." She looked up quickly to see the impact of her words. But Scott was gone, and she stood alone in the deserted corridor.

Lucille stood there a few moments, regretting her words and wondering if Scott had heard them. An orderly passed her, pushing a cart of dirty linen toward the laundry closet. Lucille glanced at her watch and remembered that Mrs. Pendleton's line needed cleansing about now. She headed back up the corridor.

Downstairs, in the parking lot, someone sat in a darkened Mustang, hunched over the steering wheel, crying his heart out. Later, Scott would write in his journal:

I just sat in the car and cried and cried—partly for Jeff and his family and partly for me and mine.

Eventually, I found my way to the last half of my support group. They need me there; I have a responsibility to them, in good times and bad. It just seems so weird, drawing close to those people when the very thing that brought us together was the common fact of our dying. . . .

SIXTEEN

Close Calls

A hot July breeze swept over flat, parched land that stretched more miles than the eye could see. The desert was dotted with cacti, scraggly shrubs, and an occasional wildflower—the only things hardy enough to survive this unforgiving, angry stretch of earth. Dry river beds and the whitewashed bones of small animals preached the harshness of the land. Frailty and weakness were not tolerated in the 110 degree temperatures or on the sands swept by hot winds. Only fortitude and virility extended life beneath the scorching sun.

Under a cloudless heaven, a ribbon of asphalt cut through the white chalky desert bed, past a forest of wind turbines harnessing the rampant desert winds, and toward an oasis in the wilderness where, at seven o'clock on a Friday night, the hot, dry desert air swirled around a smattering of shoppers on Palm Springs' downtown streets.

A teenager in a hot rod rumbled down the main drag with stereo blasting, passing two couples window shopping beneath a flamingo-pink twilight sky.

Lauren squeezed Scott's shoulder as she pointed to a shirt in a brightly lit shop window. Chuck and Gail strolled a few steps behind, licking ice cream cones and talking easily.

"They make a cute couple," Gail whispered to her husband, gesturing toward Scott and Lauren with her cone. "One time

Scott told me he thinks he and Lauren might become more than friends . . . if he ever gets well."

Ten steps ahead of Gail and Chuck, Scott and Lauren walked in near silence, stopping now and then to peer into shops. Scott's baggy T-shirt flapped in the breeze and his bony legs stuck out of oversized shorts like sticks of chalk. His white skin looked even whiter against the backdrop of tanned tourists and tanner locals.

Scott was quiet that evening. Despite the easy-going, insouciant atmosphere, he was morose and sullen. It had been one year since his diagnosis. In some ways, it had been the best year of his life; in other ways, the most harrowing.

Last week he had received the last of his disability checks. Finances were a greater concern than ever before.

In the past months, Scott had watched several friends, many from his support group, die from a variety of AIDS-induced diseases.

And then there was his own pain, and his own fears that every milestone in his life, every holiday, every family vacation, might be the last of its kind. Scott's most recent journal entry read:

I'm so tired of all this. It's been a whole year now, and I feel as though I've had about as much pain and frustration as I can take. At this point, I'm praying that God will either heal me or end my life quickly, because I just can't go on like this much longer. . . .

On that warm, dry evening in Palm Springs, Scott might have been feeling the pressure of any combination of these things. Or maybe he was simply feeling the effects of a ravaged immune system, sputtering and choking under heavy attack.

"Let's head back to the hotel," Scott said, turning back toward his parents. "I think I'll just take it easy in my room."

Back at the hotel, Chuck, Gail, and Lauren went for a late-night swim, Scott long since turned in for the night. After ten minutes in the water, they sat on lounge chairs with towels wrapped around them and talked amiably. A huge white moon bent to eavesdrop on the conversation.

"It's so relaxing here," Lauren said. "Thanks again for inviting me."

"You're part of the family," Gail replied.

A slight breeze swelled around them, awakening goosebumps on their damp bodies.

Lauren reached for a sweatshirt a few feet away. "The Bahamas will be unbelievable," she said, pulling the shirt over her head so that her last few words were muffled. She pulled the shirt over her torso. "Did Scott tell you? I've never been anywhere like that. I can't wait."

Chuck smiled. "Can't say we've been world travelers ourselves. But when Scotty fell ill. . . ."

Chuck never finished the sentence. But Lauren understood. "Well," she stepped in, saving the silence, "it was really thoughtful for you guys to invite me along. First Palm Springs, then the Bahamas. . . . It's going to be quite a summer!"

At ten o'clock the next morning, Scott tapped on Lauren's door. From behind the door she yelled "come in" and Scott dragged himself into the room. Lauren lay on the bed reading the morning paper.

"Good morning, sleepyhead," Lauren said. "How are you feeling?"

"Not so good. Miserable actually," he answered through a gravely voice. "I think I ought to go home."

"Really? We just got here yesterday."

"I know. I'm sorry. I'm really not feeling well."

Lauren reached up and felt Scott's forehead. It was as if she set her palm on a hotplate.

"You're burning up, Scott, and not just because it's 90 degrees out." She hurried into the bathroom and returned with a cool wet towel for Scott's face. "Let's get your stuff together. I'm getting you home."

They left Chuck and Gail behind with two empty rooms and more than a few fears. The Honda carrying Scott and Lauren glided through the desert as wavy sheets of heat rose from the asphalt like a mirage. Air conditioning blasted toward Scott as he reclined in his bucket seat. From time to time, he lifted his heavy eyelids to see the searing sun pouring unrelenting wrath on a smitten land.

Scott insisted that Lauren simply drop him off at his apartment. She finally agreed, but only on the condition that Scott phone the doctor immediately. As he staggered from the car he turned, glassy-eyed, toward Lauren. "I'll handle it, Lauren," he said. "I'll see you next week."

She hesitated. "Next week? Why don't I come by tomorrow?"

"I'm not a baby. I appreciate the concern, but I like to think I can still take care of myself."

Lauren bit back a response, then agreed to honor his wish.

Two days later, on Monday, Lauren stopped by to check on Scott. She found empty soups cans cluttering the kitchen counter and a musty smell in the air. Lauren discovered Scott lying limp in bed, bathed in perspiration and more gaunt than ever. Groggy and lethargic, he spoke with broken, garbled speech. Lauren poked a thermometer under his tongue and three minutes later was shocked to find it read 104 degrees. He had not been to the doctor since the ill-fated trip to Palm Springs.

Lauren bit back hot, scolding words. She stripped Scott and set him soaking in a cold bath to bring down the temperature, then made an emergency appointment with an infectious disease specialist she knew from the hospital. Later that day, the doctor diagnosed Scott with a kidney infection and immediately admitted him into the hospital. At that point his weight had dropped from 151 pounds to 130. After a week of medication and intravenous feeding, the infection subsided and Scott was released from the hospital.

In mid-August, Chuck, Gail, Tammy, Mitch, and Lauren sailed on a five-day cruise to the Bahamas, leaving Scott at home sick in bed. The cruise tickets had been purchased with the intent of spending family time together, but the unpredictability of Scott's health had changed those plans.

Meanwhile, Scott spent most of that week in bed, too sick even to read. Gary dropped by every morning to cook Scott his favorite breakfast of eggs and fried potatoes. Sometimes the combination lured Scott to eat; sometimes Gary ended up scraping the meal in the garbage disposal. Some days Gary did laundry and cleaned house. He sat with Scott for hours at a time, talking with him and reassuring him. The one thing Gary couldn't give Scott, however, was advice. Scott had a stubborn streak, and when it came to managing his disease, he didn't like to be pushed into anything.

Hours after their cruise boat docked at San Pedro Harbor, Lauren's Honda lurched to a stop at the curb in front of Scott's apartment building. The six o'clock sun hung in the horizon, painting the underbelly of high clouds a vivid orange and yellow. Tanned from hours on the cruise ship's deck, Lauren climbed the stairs, carrying a stuffed animal and a T-shirt. She knocked and opened the door a crack.

"Scott, it's me! We just got back. I came straight from the dock. Scott?"

The apartment was gray, undecided between the brightness of day and the dark of night. It was quiet, too—not a deserted quiet, but an inhabited quiet that sets the nerves on edge. Lauren flipped on a light and set the gifts down on the couch. "Scott?" she said again.

She tiptoed through the living room, stopping long enough to shake her head at the dirty kitchen. She craned her neck toward the bedroom but could detect no stirring. She kicked the overflowing clothes hamper sitting in the middle of the hallway and lugged it to the bathroom. As she rounded the corner, the bedroom door swung open.

Lauren reeled back and gasped.

Standing before her was Scott—at least she thought it was Scott—face swollen, eyes discolored, skin mottled a deep purple. His jaw was distended like Popeye's, cheeks puffed, face smirched with plum-colored splotches. Faded eyes sunk deep, encircled by black and blue eyelids.

"Oh hi, Scott, you startled me," she said, trying her best to act nonchalant. "We just got back. I came straight over here."

What she wanted to say was, "What happened to you? Who beat you up?" But she knew what had happened and that no one had hit him. Somehow the chemotherapy or the medication or the disease itself had inflated and discolored his face radically. Still, she could hardly mask the shock at his repellent appearance.

"So how was the trip?" Scott mumbled through bloated lips.

"I'll tell you all about it in a second," she replied, stepping backward toward the door. "I've got to go get something out of the car first."

Lauren shut the door behind her and ran down the stairs. All at once, her eyes laked and runnels of tears streaked toward her mouth. She locked herself in the haven of her car shaking, rocking, hands blanketing her face, the taste of salt on her trembling lips.

Later that night, Gary and Lauren accompanied Scott to St. Luke's. Gail and Chuck joined them there. They all met with Dr. Wilson Forrester, the oncologist who had been treating Scott's Kaposi's Sarcoma with chemotherapy. Somehow the doctor's graying temples, large frame, and professorial voice gave Scott confidence in him. He examined Scott thoroughly before calling Chuck, Gail, Gary, and Lauren into the treatment room.

"Kaposi's Sarcoma sometimes attacks the lymph nodes around the face," he said, lightly touching the spot under Scott's jawbone. "This inhibits the normal draining of fluids from the face. Combined with chemotherapy, all the fluids were trapped in your facial tissue, creating the swelling you see."

They discussed the situation further, until the doctor brought up a new topic.

"As long as you're all here, I'd like to make a decision regarding Interferon," he said. "The drug is now available, and we can begin treatment immediately."

"What can we expect to happen, doctor?" Chuck asked.

"Interferon is an immune system stimulator. We hope it will heighten the response of Scott's immune system to fight off the virus. It's still experimental—approved for other forms of cancer but not KS—but early studies with AIDS patients have proved positive."

"Dr. Forrester, I mentioned this to my parents several weeks ago after reading about it in a journal," Scott said. "We'll need to talk about more, but I think we're going to do it."

"Now, to be fully effective," Dr. Forrester continued, "the treatment will need to run a twelve-week cycle. And I need to be up-front with you—it's quite expensive. The first few weeks of Interferon will cost a thousand dollars a week. As dosage increases, so will the cost. Up to three thousand a week."

The room fell silent. Scott stared down at the white linoleum floor, shaking his head. Chuck's eyes narrowed and lines formed on his forehead. Gail shifted her weight and continued to look at the doctor.

"Mom, Dad, that's just too much money," Scott said in a somber tone. "Insurance won't cover it, you know, because it's experimental. I can't ask you to pay that kind of money. You've done so much already. It's just too much."

Chuck spoke up immediately: "Son, you concentrate on getting well. You do what you can, and we'll do what we have to."

Two weeks later Scott began Interferon injections.

The first few days of September prolonged August's mild weather, spurring the hopes of firefighters, freeway commuters, and others that the month's typically scorching heat would forget to show. But by the first week into September, humid air and fierce temperatures arrived on Southern California's doorstep—with plans to stay. In millions of homes and offices from San Diego to Santa Barbara air conditioners were cranked up, staving off the heat with fragile envelopes of cool air.

Scott's tiny apartment had neither air conditioning nor good cross ventilation. One Thursday night, late in the month, Scott spent the evening watching TV in the company of a box-fan, battling the heat unsuccessfully. Finally, around eight, he gave up and went to bed, lying on top of his sheets, squirming to find a cooler position. The September heat was relentless. He shifted and twitched and heaved a sigh of frustration. It had been a rough couple days, and even the escape of sleep wouldn't come easily.

Across town, Chuck and Gail sat on the living room couch, an oscillating fan sweeping back and forth across the room. Empty iced-tea glasses sat on coasters beside them.

Unfortunately, their conversation was as heavy as the sultry air that hung like a canopy outside.

"I've been over the figures ten times now," Chuck said, grabbing a stack of papers from the coffee table. "There's not going to be enough money. "

"And there's still six more weeks," Gail said, her indomitable optimism teetering. "What are we going to do?"

Chuck thumbed through the papers, looking for . . . for what? Every way he looked at it, those papers spelled trouble. With the weekly cost of the treatment approaching three thousand dollars, Interferon had quickly absorbed every resource the Camerons had. State disability, life savings, gifts from the church and friends helped. But it wasn't enough. Not nearly enough.

"I figure, all totaled, it will cost around thirty thousand dollars." Chuck fell silent. He pulled a hankerchief from his rear pocket and dabbed his forehead.

Gail watched her husband. "Are you thinking about the house?" she finally asked. He nodded. "How soon do you think we could get our hands on the money? And can we get enough?"

He paused before speaking, mulling the answers over in his mind. "I don't know. On a second mortgage, maybe four to six weeks." He turned toward Gail. "It's not the issue of spending the money. It's never been that. I'd give everything we have. I just hope we have enough."

"Lauren, I can't take much more of this," Scott said, returning from the bathroom, having thrown up for the fourth time that day. "I feel worse than I have in months." His feet dragged as if they were sticking to the floor. He rubbed his stomach—the cancer had spread to his stomach and intestines—and grimaced.

"I know. I'm sorry. Why don't we make an appointment to see. . . ."

She was interrupted as Scott's lungs unleashed a thundering cough. Lauren hurried to his side on the couch, unable to do anything but offer sympathy. He doubled over and coughed again and again.

For six weeks Lauren had been making the daily pilgrimage to Scott's apartment, each day bearing a syringe and vial of Interferon. Soon after the treatment had begun, the swelling in Scott's face had subsided and his KS spots had improved. For a time, Scott, his family, and friends held out hope that this new treatment would battle the disease into remission.

But five days earlier, Scott's condition had taken a turn for the worse. He started vomiting everything, his temperature rose, and his cough returned with a vengeance.

"Lauren, what if the KS has spread to my lungs?" Scott sat on the couch, wrapped in a quilt. He reached for a Kleenex and wiped his nose.

"I don't know. We don't know anything," she said. "Let's just take one day at a time. You've had six strong weeks."

Despite her courageous demeanor, Lauren, too, had fears. She had seen Scott's body wither to 120 pounds. She caught glimpses of bones protruding at every joint, threatening to push through his sagging skin. His appetite had waned, and what he did eat he couldn't keep down.

"When I go see Dr. Forrester, he's going to want to admit me to the hospital," Scott said. "Lauren, I'm not going in the hospital. If I do, I won't come out."

Lauren shuddered, but when she spoke, her tone was brisk. "Scott, you're being silly. I don't want any more talk like that. I'm calling Forrester today."

The next morning, Gary and Lauren accompanied Scott to the hospital to see Dr. Forrester. As Scott predicted, the doctor recommended that Scott be admitted to St. Luke's. He explained that with IV feeding, Scott's weight would be bolstered. He could go home after he regained some strength.

As the doctor spoke, Scott remembered his prediction from yesterday and shuddered: *If I go in, I won't come out . . . won't come out . . . won't come out.*

But at Dr. Forrester's strong urging, Scott reluctantly agreed and was admitted to the hospital that night.

In the days that followed, Lauren visited Scott's hospital room before her shift began, on her breaks, and after work. She monitored every medication he took and scoured daily reports. Gary, too, stopped by every night after work, bringing mail, gifts, and encouragement.

The days passed slowly for Scott. Nagging stomach pains made food seem repulsive. He felt self-conscious about his appearance and didn't want to be seen by anyone but those closest to him. Only the faces of his family and friends wiped away moribund thoughts. Lying in the hospital bed, he offered long, sincere prayers to God. *Jesus, I've made many mistakes in my life. You've loved me just the same. Still, I'm reaping what I sowed. I plead for Your mercy. Heal me, Father. Heal me.*

"Lauren . . . don't leave," Scott said. "I'm . . . afraid."

His lips took little part in the wispy sounds that tiptoed up his throat and snuck out. The words were mere gusts of air. He lay in the hospital bed, an IV tube snaking into his left arm. His breathing was labored that night.

"It's okay," she said quietly. "I'll stay with you."

It was six o'clock on Thursday night, Scott's fifth day in St. Luke's. Lauren stood at his bed in her crisp white uniform, ready to start her shift. She lowered the steel bed rails and sat down beside him.

On the nightstand, next to the plastic water pitcher, sat a teddy bear with a note taped to it that read, "We're praying for you. You're not alone. Love, Tony and Caroline." Next to the bear bloomed a bouquet of flowers from Tammy and Mitch. And beneath a box of tissues lay a half-empty journal. Its last entry date was three months ago.

Scott, eyes closed, groped for Lauren's hand and squeezed it tight. She stared down at the bony fingers gripping her hand. Then her eyes surveyed the terrain of Scott's body. His hair, once a carpet of thick auburn waves, now drooped thin and scraggly. The wispy strands that had survived fifteen months of chemotherapy did little to conceal the flaky, mottled scalp. Silver-dollar sized purple blotches sprung from ash-white skin. The pale-blue gown that sheathed his body hung low on his chest, revealing more territory claimed by the army of KS lesions.

With her free hand, Lauren pinched the corners of her eyes, stanching the tears that threatened to spill out onto her cheeks. She took a deep breath and exhaled silently.

"I'm here, Scotty," she whispered. "I'm here."

He lay motionless. His chest rose and fell ever so slightly.

Lauren finally left to begin her shift ten minutes late, knowing that Gary would arrive soon. She spent the next few hours attending patients and passing medications. She was walking from one room to another when suddenly she stopped in her tracks. Standing stock still in the corridor, she felt an undeniable prompting to go to Scott. She notified her supervisor that she was leaving, then she hurried down to two-north.

Lauren walked past nurses chatting at the desk and cracked the door open to peek in at Scott. Gary sat in a vinyl chair holding his hand. Gary caught the light filtering through the opened door and motioned for Lauren to come in.

She grasped Scott's other hand and leaned close.

"He's been asleep since I got here two hours ago," Gary whispered. "It looks like he's hardly breathing. Is he okay?"

Lauren didn't answer. Her mind replayed the instructions Scott had given her: No heroic efforts to resuscitate him. *When it's my time to go,* he had said, *I'd rather go than be kept alive by a machine.* He had seen patients on respirators, and he knew the pain it caused. He wanted no part of it.

Minutes lingered by silently. Gary and Lauren nourished solitary thoughts and memories. Though separated by vast differences in lifestyle, faith, background, and morals, at this moment, their thoughts were parallel. Each remembered a blossoming relationship with Scott, recalled times of laughter, lamented the illness that wracked Scott's body and spirit, and feared the pain and grief of loss. One difference—one critical difference—separated their thoughts: one had known the love of this man, the other had only hoped . . . no, longed for it. Somehow the scene was metaphoric for the past year of Scott's life—one hand held by Lauren, one by Gary.

The room was dark except for a dim overhead light that glowed near the bathroom door. The low lights and the hushed atmosphere spread a monasterial aura through the room. The stillness and the loving memories flowing through the room somehow framed the scene in holiness and reverence.

Lauren looked down at the hand she was holding. She moved her thumb to rub against the fingers. She glanced up at Scott's face with a tiny smile playing on her lips.

Suddenly, she bolted to her feet.

"He's not breathing!" she shouted. "He stopped breathing!"

Gary jumped up, his face stricken with fear.

"Lower the bed," Lauren barked, fumbling for the button on the bed rail that would buzz the nurses' station. Gary dove for the crank at the foot of the bed. Lauren flung open the hospital room door. She screamed, "We need a doctor in room 12E!"

As Gary cranked Scott's bed into a horizontal position, Lauren checked his breathing again. Nothing. She lifted an eyelid to find a dilated pupil. His eye was rolled up, vacant and glassy. She'd seen it all before, many times. Scott's pupils were dilated because oxygen wasn't getting to his brain.

"I love you, Scott," she said into his ear. "We're here for you. Hang on."

A few seconds later, a doctor whooshed into the room. He brushed Lauren aside, checked Scott's pulse and pupils, then snapped at one of the nurses who'd followed him in: "Narcan!" The nurse produced a needle. The doctor grabbed Scott's arm, jabbed the needle into a vein, and emptied the syringe. He lifted an eyelid.

Lauren and Gary backed away as still more nurses and orderlies flew into the room.

"What is it?" Gary asked Lauren. "What's happening?"

Lauren remained silent, staring at the knot of technicians hovering over Scott.

Words and instructions were uttered quietly, firmly within the circle. A nurse broke from the cluster, scurried from the room, and returned in a few seconds carrying an oxygen tank.

Lauren ran to the phone at the nurses' module. She dialed the number for Chuck and Gail. "You'd better hurry. . . . Yes, now."

Tense minutes passed as Gary looked on, frantic but helpless.

One by one, nurses and orderlies filed from the room. The doctor walked over to Gary and Lauren. He looked relieved.

"What happened?" Gary asked. "Is he all right?"

"You knew that a plural effusion had formed beneath his left lung, constricting the lung and making breathing painful. A few hours ago we tapped into it," the doctor explained, "to drain the fluid beneath his lung so he could breathe easier. We gave him anesthetic—Demerol. He must have reacted to the dosage. His system apparently couldn't handle it."

"And the injection just now?" Gary asked.

"Narcan, to reverse the affects of the narcotic Demerol," he replied. "Scott's going to be fine."

Before long, Scott began to stir. Awakening, he let out a low moan. Gary and Lauren stood close, squeezing his hands, rubbing his shoulders and reassuring him. Several minutes later, Scott began to speak.

"Thes . . ." he forced from his lungs. "Thesm. . . ."

Gary and Lauren leaned in, trying to decipher his babel.

"The . . . smell," he said, finally understandable. "The smell."

Standing beside the bed, Gary and Lauren turned toward each other with puzzled looks. The smell? What did it mean? Lauren wondered: *Had Scott, for a few fleeting moments, crossed over to the afterlife? Had he seen Heaven?*

"What do you mean, Scott?" Gary asked quietly. "What smell?"

Scott, still struggling to focus his eyes, turned his head toward Gary's voice. "I can't stand the smell," he eked out the words. "I . . . I crapped all over myself."

Lauren stifled a small laugh. She called an orderly, then wet a wash cloth to begin cleaning Scott up. Gary helped.

"You guys must really love me," Scott managed to say, "to do this."

"Did you ever doubt it?" Lauren asked.

Gail, Chuck, Tammy, Lauren, and Gary spent the night in Scott's room, drifting in and out of sleep, curled on the empty bed, a cot, and stiff vinyl chairs. By seven o'clock the next morning, word had circulated throughout the hospital about Scott's brush with death.

Around nine o'clock Nick, Scott's former boss, stood outside the door to Scott's room. With his muscular physique, rugged looks, and thick brown mustache, Nick looked like he should have been leaning against a horse corral or a football locker instead of the nurses' station. He was, in fact, known to his coworkers as an intrepid outdoorsman and athlete. He and Scott had a cordial, but not close, working relationship. Nick was a Christian, but for years had fallen away, experimenting with every form of immorality. He had returned to God just months earlier with a fire in his heart that blazed unmistakably.

Finally the door opened, and Tammy strolled out rubbing blurry eyes. She looked up, then blinked and rubbed her eyes again before sneaking a second stare.

There, just yards from Scott's room, stood a husky man in green hospital garb, weeping openly and sending fervent prayers to God.

For the next three days, Gail, Chuck, and Lauren lived in Scott's hospital room, keeping vigil day and night. In the midnight hours, Gail and Lauren shared the empty hospital bed next to Scott's, and Chuck slept in a chair next to the window. Each morning he awoke in excruciating pain, working the kinks out of arthritic limbs, but he never complained.

On the fourth evening, Scott sent his parents home to their bed, but he asked Lauren if she would stay. Scott didn't want to be alone. Gary visited once, sometimes twice, each day, and his visits always cheered Scott. But in the scary midnight hours, when the fears of dying loomed largest, Scott needed Lauren.

One stormy Wednesday evening, three weeks into Scott's hospital stay, Scott and Lauren were playing a round of cards.

Sheets of rain flung themselves at the window, which framed a small piece of the night behind sterile white mini-blinds. A strong gust of wind rattled the pane, set in the second floor of St. Luke's sprawling facility.

Lauren, sitting in a chair next to Scott's bed, glanced at the blinds. "Wild night out there," she said.

Scott nodded, but didn't speak. He was learning to save his energy for things that mattered.

Like, of course, winning. A moment later he laid a spread of cards on the over-bed table that sat poised between him and Lauren. "Gin rummy," he announced with no small amount of pleasure.

Lauren scooped up the cards, shuffled, and began to redeal in one determined sweep. "Five and five," she said. "This one breaks the tie."

Suddenly a twist of the wind flung a new wave of rain against the window. The roar of water pummeling the building drowned out any possibility of conversation. Lauren finished dealing the cards in silence. Scott was the first to speak, struggling to raise his voice above the elements.

"Hope Mom and Dad get back safe," he said.

"Where did they go? Little Caesar's?" Lauren sorted her hand as she answered. "It's not far. They'll be fine. I just hope the pizza stays dry. And you, Scott Cameron, are going to eat this time. No excuses." She flashed him her Gestapo-look over her cards.

Scott raised one hand in a weak salute. "Yes, Nurse." He arranged the cards in his hands, breaking the silence a few moments later. "Hey, Lauren . . . doesn't it feel like we're a couple of ol' married folk?"

By then the wind had died down, and the sound of the rain had dropped from deafening to merely drumming loudly. The rain, still sheeting just beyond the mini-blinds, made the room feel cozy—the pelting against the window a constant reminder that there was nowhere else to be right at that very moment.

Lauren leaned against the back of her chair and studied Scott. She didn't answer his question.

Scott continued, "Look at us, sitting here playing gin rummy like we've done it a million times instead of only once. It's so comfortable, natural, cozy—like it's . . . right."

Lauren leaned forward and answered in a tone that was almost brusque. "It's the rain, Scott. You're just feeling the effects of the rain."

Scott laid his cards down on the table. The cards were face up, and Lauren saw the entire hand. But Scott didn't seem to notice or to care. He lay, skinny and scarred by the cancer, bolstered by a half dozen pillows. But he watched Lauren with an intensity in his eyes that Lauren hadn't seen before.

"No. It's not the rain. Mom and I talked about it a couple of days ago. I mean, you're with me when I fall asleep at night; you're the first thing I see in the morning. You wash my hair, give me my baths. The only times you leave me are to go home and shower or to go work for a few hours at a time. Lauren, I've always wanted to be loved like this. I used to pray, 'God, before I die, I want to know what it's like for someone to really, truly love me. Not my parents—but someone besides them.'"

Lauren felt her eyes sting. "Scott, don't. . . ."

"Don't tell me to stop. I've got to say this. Lauren, I know I've always loved you—somehow, despite the fact that my feelings were all twisted up inside. But I never realized how much I loved you until now, when you've given up everything for me. And I know you'd give even more—if there was anything else to give. And I want you to know, Lauren. I've made a decision."

Lauren felt weak. She managed to eke out a "What?"

"If God heals me," Scott said with conviction, ". . . if God heals me, we're getting married. I want to marry you."

SEVENTEEN

No Time for Games

"You what?" Lauren choked on the words.

"Think about it!" Scott's words rushed out in an torrent, his excitement pushing back the strongholds of the virus, reclaiming for the moment a little bit of ground—a little bit of life—that had been lost to the enemy in the past couple of months. "We'll have the most perfect marriage, Lauren. We love each other, and if we can make it through this AIDS thing, we can make it through anything. We won't have in-law problems, that's for sure, because my parents already love you and your parents love me, too. And I'll see a psychologist about my sexual problems. I'll see someone and get it all worked out, and it'll be fine. You'll see. We can be happy, Lauren."

Lauren just stared, the storm outside the mini-blinds suddenly mild compared to the storm raging in her heart. The words had come too late. Lauren knew Scott was dying; Scott knew he was dying. They would never become that little family. *God,* she pleaded, *to have heard these words two years ago.*

Yet her heart pounded doubletime, and despite her grief, she felt the stirrings of her own hope and excitement rising to meet Scott's. Scott loved her; her love had changed him. That, in itself, was nearly miracle enough. Who was she to doubt the future?

Lauren nodded, a smile was burgeoning on her lips, her

hands were clasped tightly together in front of her. "All right," she said, "all right. I'll marry you."

That weekend, Gail, Chuck, and Gary moved Scott's belongings out of his apartment on Colorado Street. The comic books, photo albums, clothes, and meager furnishings went back to the little brick and stucco house where Scott had grown up. On Saturday, ACE Medical Rental delivered a hospital bed to that same house, two brawny deliverymen carrying pieces of the bed through the living room, past the couch, chairs, end tables, and TV crammed into half the space they had once taken. Gail and Chuck had cleared the northwest corner of the living room, near a mirrored wall and across the room from the big picture window. Scott's bed would go there.

Scott came home on Monday, the fourth day of October. Lauren came with him. As a nurse, she would be invaluable with Scott's homecare; as a woman in love, she wanted to be near him at any cost.

Monday afternoon, Lauren was at her own apartment, collecting a few personal items to take with her back to Gail and Chuck's home. Chuck was still at work, as was Gary. But Gail was home, having taken the day off work to be with Scott.

At 3:00, Gail was puttering around the house, trying to organize her displaced furniture as well as a stack of Scott's belongings, freshly moved from his apartment.

She picked up a box of letters and computer printouts and approached the hospital bed in the corner where Scott lay resting, his back to the wall.

"Scott, where do you want me to put these letters? In the spare room? Toss them? What?"

Scott struggled to sit up higher and peered into the box. "Spare room's fine, Mom." He lay back down and closed his eyes.

Gail turned to go, box in hand, when something caught her eye. She stopped, reached into the box, and touched the return address on one of the envelopes. "Duane Slifka," she read aloud. "Wasn't that the boy who wrote to Spatula Ministries? The boy struggling with homosexuality? So you wrote to him after all."

Scott opened his eyes and nodded. "Been writing for months."

"What did you tell him, Scott?" Gail asked, her curiosity rising like a tide. Months ago, Scott felt he had few answers and little wisdom to share with Duane. But a lot had changed since then. Scott's health had plummeted; but Gail sensed changes on a larger scale as well. She repeated her question to Scott. "What did you finally tell him?"

"I'll show you sometime."

"Show me?"

"Yeah. I wrote the letters on the computer. I think some of my responses to him are probably in the box."

Gail started to comment again, but when she looked at Scott, she saw he was resting again, his eyes closed.

She turned and headed into the hallway toward the spare room that once was Tammy's. Gail found an empty space on one of the bookshelves and raised her arms to slide the box of letters next to the kids' old encyclopedia set.

Suddenly she stopped. Lowering her arms, she stared into the box, debating. After all, Scott had promised to show her the letters.

Gail pulled the box onto her lap and sat on the edge of Tammy's bed. She found the computer printouts: There were letters to different friends, as well as some journal entries dated six months earlier. She skipped the journal entries and the letters that Scott hadn't given permission for her to read. She went right to a series of a half-dozen letters addressed to Duane.

Gail read them all. In the end there was one letter in particular that embedded itself in her memory, giving her new insight into the man she called her son.

Scott had written:

The thought of death isn't all that terrifying, actually. As you know (as someone who's been there), it hasn't been such an easy life, so the thought of a life in Heaven, with perfect love and no guilt or confusion, sounds pretty good! What I'm concerned with is living the time I have left for the Lord. There's really no time for games now; everything must count.

For the first time, I'm finding myself almost glad that this has all happened—isn't that strange? Because of all this, I've developed a close relationship with my family and learned to love them all the more. I've learned that I have Christian friends who really do love me, in good or bad times. And most importantly, I'm learning that, with God's help, I can do so much more than I ever thought I could. These are hard times; it takes a lot of courage and determination to get through it all—and I still don't have all the answers about my homosexuality and my future. But I really like the person that I'm becoming through all this.

And as he closed the letter, Scott encouraged Duane with a single sentence that somehow said it all:

Stay pure, and don't give up hope.

Gail refolded the pages and replaced them in the box. She stood on tiptoe and slid the box next to the encyclopedias. Before she left the spare room, she smoothed the dimple on the bedspread where she'd been sitting, then drew the shades on the windows. She closed the door as she left, quietly, reverently, in the manner of someone leaving a chapel where they've just caught a glimpse of the power of God at work in a human heart

Thursday morning dawned with passion, the twilight blushing into brilliance. At the Midas touch of the sun's bright fingers, one quiet, tree-lined street in the suburbs of Los Angeles shimmered like white gold, the frost-laden lawns that lined that street suddenly transformed into carpets of glittering crystals.

From where she slept on the couch beside a sunlit picture window, Lauren stirred. Her eyelids fluttered. When she opened her eyes, the livingroom was bright. She stretched her legs, then turned her body on the narrow couch, shifting her back to the window and pulling the blanket higher around her neck. She nuzzled into her pillow.

But just as she closed her eyes, she heard a voice, and her heart gave a small leap at the sound: "Good morning, Sweetheart."

Lauren turned and focused her eyes on Scott, who was watching her from his hospital bed across the room. "You're awake early," she managed to say calmly, even though the heart of a rabbit never beat as quickly as hers beat at that very moment.

"Couldn't sleep." Scott's words were followed up by a thunderous round of gravely coughs emitted from disease-riddled lungs.

"Want some breakfast?" Lauren asked, sleep suddenly at the bottom of her list of priorities.

Scott shook his head. "Nah, my stomach's hurting again."

"You're just saying that because you've heard the rumors about my cooking," Lauren teased, trying to recapture a lighter mood.

Scott smiled. He feigned surprise. "You mean you don't have notches on your frying pan?"

Lauren picked up her pillow and threatened to toss it at Scott. He raised a bony arm to ward off the attack. But it never came. Sometimes, looking at Scott, Lauren had the frightening thought that Scott's frail body might crumble, like an ash sculpture, with even the slightest touch.

She dropped the pillow back on the couch, then climbed from beneath her blankets in the red sweats she'd worn to bed last night.

As Lauren searched in a small overnight bag for her makeup and toothbrush, Scott watched. After a moment, he spoke: "I've made a decision."

Lauren smiled, still searching. "All these decisions lately."

"This one's different."

"Go on."

"I always wanted . . ." his words were interrupted by yet another sequence of coughs. Lauren waited patiently. Scott found his voice again. "I've always wanted to write a book, Lauren. I'm beginning to think it'll never happen."

Lauren left the bag on the floor, abandoning the makeup for the moment. She walked across the room, sitting in a chair next to Scott's bed. "I'm listening."

"That's pretty much it. Except I'm starting to wonder if there's not something that still needs to be said. What if . . . what if I did a tape—an interview kind of thing—with a pastor or something."

"You have someone in mind?"

"Yeah. Pastor Miller. He was my pastor the whole time I was growing up, before my family changed churches when I was a sophomore in high school."

"Do you want me to help arrange it?" Lauren asked.

Scott nodded, staring absently down at the purple cancer lesions spotting his arms and body. "I guess I thought I was immune, you know? But I learned the hard way. There are consequences to our choices. And sometimes they're pretty scary."

Pastor Miller arrived on Saturday, tape recorder in hand. He was a big man, in his early forties, with a genuine smile and a thatch of salt-and-pepper hair. He greeted the family warmly, and grasped Scott's hand in a firm grip. "I'm here, my friend," he said, pulling up a chair.

Pastor Miller opened with a short prayer, asking God's blessings on their conversation. The two men small-talked for a few moments. Finally the pastor asked how Scott's struggle with homosexuality began.

Scott thought back through the years. "Maybe it had something to do with the fact that I was sick all the time, so all my friends were girls—the boys didn't like me. I seemed to feel more pressure than usual to be liked by men."

"Did you ever talk to anyone about it?"

Scott shook his head. "No. But now I wish I had. I'm convinced that homosexuality wasn't my problem; it was the answer I used to deal with underlying problems about my self-image, about how others saw me, how I saw myself. The roots went deep, and the pain. . . . I think even if I had stopped dating men and doing the surface stuff, the problems would have still been there—with my self-image, with all the desires that were wrong, yet seemed so right."

"While you were involved in homosexuality, did you ever sense God's Spirit drawing you away from that?"

Scott smiled. "I always knew He was there. In fact the first time I went to the gay bath, I was walking toward the door and I just had a feeling—almost a voice—that said, 'Scott, you can turn around. This is a threshold, and you don't have to cross it.' God was always there, offering me something different, but I wouldn't take it. I was afraid to trust. And then I got trapped."

Pastor Miller cleared his throat. "What could the church have done . . . well, let me ask it this way. How would you encourage someone, if you knew they were struggling, wondering about their own identity. . . ."

Scott never hesitated. "What I would have wanted someone to tell me is that you can still be effective for God even if you have these feelings; it's not the end of the world—there is hope. God has an alternative. For me, I didn't choose to have those feelings; but I did choose to act on them.

"Look," Scott added, "this may not be a popular thought among Christians, but . . . I don't think the church teaches the right survival techniques. We keep saying 'don't fall, don't have premarital sex, don't do this or that. . . .' Yet I think there needs to be some emphasis on a second message that says, 'Okay so you've blown it. Now where do you go from here? Do you just give up?'"

Pastor Miller nodded. "So we need to strive harder to be a hospital for the wounded; and if someone is wounded with any kind of wound, we've got to be there to help them repair that. So if a person's done drugs or had an abortion or whatever, the attitude needs to be, 'Come on in, we want to help you'—even if that person is a Christian."

Scott pointed a finger at the pastor. "Exactly. I was always afraid I would be kicked out of the church. One time one of the church secretaries, Pam Simmons, called me in the office and said, 'I know there's something in you that you won't talk about, something that I sense really hurts you.'"

"And what happened?" Pastor Miller asked.

"I came this close to telling her . . . but the fear was just so great."

"What's different now? Obviously you can talk about it now."

Scott shrugged. "I guess I had to get to a point where being honest and walking forward with God was greater than anything else I feared."

"And the things you feared . . . have they happened?"

Scott stared out the window for a moment. "There has been some rejection, from some friends, from one pastor. . . . But I've discovered friends who really love me, and there really is nothing I could do to make them stop loving me. And that really motivates me to live for God." Scott turned back to Pastor Miller and his eyes were blazing. "You know, it's not just homosexuality. It could be drugs, promiscuity, adultery, embezzlement . . . who knows? People need to know there's nothing they can do that is going to take away the kind of love that is meant to last—love from God, from their church, from their family."

"Scott, you mentioned to me over the phone that having a disease like this has brought an added awareness of God in your life. Tell me more about that."

"It's simple. I don't have time to play games; I don't have time to pussyfoot around. If I'm going to live for the Lord, I have to do it now; because there's no promise of tomorrow for me. I think a lot of what I went through was avoidable. If I could help someone else by laying myself bare, and just telling them what it's like . . then that's important. Face it: Sin is fun. It's exciting. But it doesn't last. It doesn't offer eternal rewards, and it leaves you feeling really hollow; God doesn't leave you feeling that way."

"So you sense a real fulfillment in your life and your spirit now?" Pastor Miller asked the question for the benefit of anyone who might one day listen to the tape—but he didn't need to hear the answer himself. He could read it on Scott's face as he talked about God's new place in his life.

Scott was emphatic. "Definitely. I was so trapped; I couldn't have gotten out of it if I wanted to, and part of me still didn't want to. I always knew God would have to deal drastically with me. I didn't know how He would—and I'm sorry He had to—but I consider it a sign of His love that He didn't just let me go, that He found a way to bring me back, even if that way means dying of AIDS. You know, I've been a Christian half my life; I know the Bible, I know what it says. But it's just . . . it's real now. It has to be. It's my hope."

Scott paused, thinking. Pastor Miller watched in silence, waiting for Scott's next words. Scott finally said, "I just hope that if someone hears about my story, they won't judge me or say, 'That couldn't happen to me.' I just hope people realize that if it isn't homosexuality in their lives, it's probably something else. Satan wants Christians, and he'll find *something*—any toehold."

"And yet I did fail," he added. "I failed miserably. I blew it. But rather than wallow in it and say, 'There's no hope, I can't be a Christian. . . .' I've chosen to repent, to get back on my feet and live for Jesus. It's never too late to do that."

"What about your gay friends who don't know the Lord?" Pastor Miller asked. "Do you have a chance to share with them?"

"Yeah, they visit and they ask questions." For the first time in the forty-minute interview, a shadow of pain darted across Scott's eyes. He continued, "There's one special friend, Gary. He believes in God, but he's not too sure about Jesus. You know, if he came to know the Lord, it would mean so very much to me. . . ."

Scott added, "I'll tell you how it is that I'm so sure that Jesus Christ is where it's at; that Christianity is where the rubber hits the road. It's the fact that my family and friends know all my darkest secrets, and yet they love me more than ever before. If they love me that much, I know that God must love me all the more."

Pastor Miller left with a cassette tape—and Scott's one shot at ministry—tucked under his arm.

A few hours later, Scott received a second visitor—a nurse who put Scott on a morphine drip—and his thoughts were forcibly jolted back to the body that was deteriorating around him.

The bag of morphine, strung up on an IV stand, fed Scott constant minuscule doses of the powerful drug to help combat the pain that was fast becoming his most intimate and constant companion. In the following days, Tammy and Gary visited daily, and Tony and Caroline Lozano stopped by often. Scott began to sleep a lot, drugged and groggy from the morphine. When he was awake, he read books or watched TV or visited with friends in a house that Gail kept dark and quiet.

Gary had just arrived one evening when Scott suddenly yelped in surprise and pain. Lauren was at his side immediately, Gary just behind her.

Scott looked up, fear in his eyes, and said simply, "The mattress is soaked."

Lauren relaxed her muscles visibly. "Oh, is *that* all? I thought something was wrong. Gary, help me move Scott to the couch. . . ."

"It's not that," Scott blurted. "I didn't have an accident. There's something wrong with my stomach."

Gary drew back the sheets to reveal a tiny puncture in the wall of Scott's abdomen, which had recently become swollen. From the hole, clear yellow fluid was draining in small gushes.

Lauren studied the new development. "A fistula," she announced.

"To relieve the pressure?" Scott asked.

Lauren nodded. Lauren, Gary, and Scott, each employed in hospitals, realized what had happened. Lauren immediately called to Gail, who was sewing in the spare room, for more dressings, bed sheets, and pajamas.

As she and Gary changed the sheets, Lauren explained to Gail that Scott's body had created its own valve to relieve the building pressure of body fluids.

In the next several hours, Scott's bandages, clothes, and sheets had to be changed numerous times. By afternoon the next day, a nurse arrived from Scott's doctor's office. She brought Hollister bags into which the fluid could drain. By the time the nurse left, Scott was resting quietly, the living room drapes drawn, the ringer on the phone flipped to mute. Lauren emptied the fluid from the bag, rehung Scott's IV, and administered his drugs. Gail hovered around Scott's bed, offering small sips of juice or a few bites of food—whatever Scott felt well enough to handle. The days passed, the autumn sun rising and setting in the world beyond the Cameron home. Scott, sleeping away the hours in a darkened, silent house, began to lose track of the passage of time.

October in Southern California is an indecisive month. Santa Ana winds sometimes persist well past Columbus Day, chapping lips, prompting brisk sales of hand lotion, creating fire hazards. Other years, October escorts in the winter chill, denuding trees, reddening noses, and resurrecting whole herds of closeted wool sweaters.

There was no indecision about October 1986. It was downright cold.

Just after dinner on Halloween evening, Gary showed up on the doorstep wearing a flight jacket with the collar hugging his neck. But as she swung open the front door that wasn't the thing that caught Tammy's attention or made the two-year-old son in her arms squeal with glee.

Gary wore a hyena-grin beneath his white-blond moustache, and beneath each arm he balanced a bright pumpkin. "Trick or treat!" he bellowed as Matthew struggled from his mother's arms. Dropping to the floor, Matthew rushed to the screen door, laughing and shouting, "Punkins! Punkins!"

The noise drew Gail from the kitchen, dish towel in hand. "Keep it down, guys, Scott's rest. . . ."

Gary, inside now, swept past Gail in a swirl of cool air. He deposited the pumpkins on the little formica table. "Scott's always resting, Gail," he said warmly. "He can rest later. Right now it's time for some fun."

Gary sent Tammy scrambling for newspapers, then dragged the little kitchen table next to Scott's hospital bed. He handed a child's safety knife to Matthew, who perched wide-eyed in his chair, sitting on his knees, eyeing the pumpkins impatiently.

Lauren cranked Scott to a sitting position, where his eyes

danced as he watched Gary and Matthew carve funny faces in the fat orange gourds. Tammy gave advice, and even Chuck broke in with a suggestion or two from where he sat reading the paper on the couch. And for the first time in a good two weeks, Scott's parents heard him laugh . . . actually laugh.

Gail had to smile as she returned to the dishes in the kitchen. "Did you see the boys?" she said to Lauren, who stood scraping cole slaw from a serving bowl into Tupperware. "Matthew reminds me so much of Scott—a little redheaded boy sitting there carving pumpkins. . . ."

Lauren burped the Tupperware with deliberation. Gail didn't seem to notice.

Gail cracked open the refrigerator door to put away a tub of margarine. "Maybe I have kept the place too quiet the past couple of weeks. Maybe Gary's right; maybe Scott doesn't need quiet as much as he needs life and laughter and a good dose of zaniness now and then. But how was I supposed to know? I've never been in this kind of situation. . . ."

Suddenly Gail stopped talking and eyed Lauren, who was wiping the stovetop with the washrag, her eyes averted and lips pressed into a thin line. "What's wrong, Lauren? Something's wrong."

Lauren threw the washrag angrily into the sink. Her eyes darted toward the living room. She lowered her voice. "It's . . it's Gary," she hissed.

"Lauren . . . honey . . ." Gail began but trailed off, unsure of what to say.

Lauren looked down at her hands, now twisting nervously. "Oh, I've grown to appreciate him, as I know you have, too. He's a really sweet, caring person, who just happens to need a relationship with Jesus Christ. And he loves Scott. He really does."

Gail just listened.

"But I don't understand. I don't understand any of it. I mean, why's he still here? Why does Scott still encourage the friendship? Scott says he loves me; he says he wants to marry me. Yet he never sends Gary away. Sometimes I don't know where I stand. Where Gary stands. Where Scott stands."

Gail let her eyes roam toward the window, past the hang-ing beads and on into the night. Suddenly she turned back to Lauren, mustered a bold smile, and reached out to squeeze Lauren's hand. "I don't think Scott knows either," she said. "Not yet, anyway. It takes time to sort out the matters of a heart that is this new to the light. Give him time."

Time, Lauren thought with a bitter residue, *if only I could give time. . . .*

Gary left around nine. After he left, Gail and Chuck gave goodnight kisses all around and turned in for the night. Lauren escaped into the bathroom to change into her sweats, and Tammy began to round up Matthew's things. Matthew himself lay curled and sleeping at the foot of the couch.

"Tammy," Scott said, his voice dragging with exhaustion. "Come here. I gotta ask a favor."

When Tammy approached, Scott's voice got even softer. "About Gary. He doesn't know Jesus—personally, I mean."

"I know."

"Well, we've had plenty of discussions about religion, that's for sure. But I know I wasn't always the greatest example. Any-way, I don't think I'm the one who can make the final points with Gary and help him find eternal life. So, after I die.   ."

"Scott, don't say things like. . . ."

"Tammy, hush," Scott said tenderly. "Look. When I die, fol-low up with Gary, okay? It might be a good time to talk to him about his own life—about his own eternity. Even if he and I can never be more than friends, that doesn't stop me from caring a lot about what happens to him and to his soul."

"Scott, is he in danger?"

"Danger?" Scott repeated.

"Of dying with AIDS."

Scott managed a small smile. "No. That's me."

"I mean later, knucklehead. What if he has the virus, too?"

"I don't know. He says he doesn't; he says it's not in his karma to die of AIDS. But the fact is, no one knows. The virus can be latent for five to ten years."

"Can't he be tested? Isn't there an AIDS test or something?"

"Sure, but it's hardly perfect. I tested negative long after I was diagnosed with Kaposi's Sarcoma—at my age a sure sign of AIDS. So will you remember Gary?"

"I'll remember."

Later, after Tammy and Matthew had returned home to Mitch and the Cameron household began settling into sleep, the living room was dark as Scott heard Lauren throw back the blanket on the couch and lie down. The headlights from a passing car reflected on the wall a moment and then were gone. Scott looked toward the couch, but the room was already dark again and he couldn't see a thing.

He heard Lauren shift. He heard a small sigh.

And then he said, just as he had said every night for the past three weeks, "Goodnight, Sweetheart. I love you."

And from across the room, the words came back small and slightly muffled from the pillow Lauren hoped would hide her tears, "I love you, too, Scott."

Scott's thirtieth birthday dawned on Wednesday, November thirteenth.

In the following week, Chuck continued dealing with his grief and expressing his love for Scott by running errands. He kept the house stocked with popsicles and Jell-O—anything the family could get Scott to swallow. Scott was down to 115 pounds, his five foot eleven frame gaunt and hollow.

Gary's visits continued. He and Lauren took turns helping Scott to the bathroom, emptying the bag on his fistula, and turning him in bed to avoid bedsores. Lauren walked Scott around the house, dragging the IV, taking him into the kitchen, passing the little formica table, and peering into the refrigerator—not so much because Scott could be tempted to eat, but simply for a change of scenery.

Scott gave his parents his latest journal . . . the one with the blue-sky cover—the one that he'd written for them. Chuck blinked back the tears. Gail put the journal in safe place, waiting for the time when she would have the strength to read it. Scott and Tammy spent hours talking about Scott's latest goal: he wanted to start a ministry to pastors, helping them understand how to best counsel Christians struggling with homosexuality. Finally, Lauren spent her time encouraging Scott to hang on to life, to continue fighting the cancer and other diseases that were invading his defenseless system.

One night, a week past Scott's birthday, Lauren lay awake through most of the midnight hours listening to Scott's raspy breathing as he struggled, half conscious, to fill his lungs with air. Around six in the morning, just as the night was graying toward the dawn, she climbed from beneath warm blankets and padded across the cool living room. She knelt at the edge of Scott's bed, taking his cancer-scarred hand in her hand.

"Scott," she whispered.

He stirred ever so slightly.

"Scott, I know I've been telling you to hang on," Lauren's lips trembled as she spoke. "I know what I've told you—and you've done it, too. You've done great, Scott. No one could have done more." She laid her cheek against Scott's hand, her strawberry-blonde hair falling across her face as she did. A tear slipped down her cheek.

The dark room grew dusky with the dawn. Lauren swallowed hard. A second tear joined the first. "Scott, I just wanted you to know. . . ." She took a deep breath, praying as she formed the words, "I wanted you to know that you don't have to hang on anymore. It's okay to let go."

Scott's breath was coming faintly.

Lauren touched his face, mottled by the cancer. She had some "letting go" of her own to do. There would be dreams to bury. . . .

She shook her head, dislodging the thoughts of her loss. She couldn't think of that—not yet. She needed to think of Scott, think about what was the best thing for Scott.

And suddenly Lauren smiled.

She actually smiled at a tiny ray of a thought . . . the flickering light of a single thought that held the potential of scattering the gloom of even the deepest pit. The light started in the depths of her soul and spread, warming, brightening as it grew, until it even began to thaw the ice-hot pain of her grieving heart.

And Lauren basked in the simple realization: Scott—who had never known, all at the same time, the integrity of spirit, mind, and body—was about to make a discovery. He stood poised at the threshold of the brightest chapter of his life. And despite her grief, Lauren harbored no doubts about the future: The best part of Scott's story awaited, just a heartbeat away. . .

Scott Cameron died three hours later,
surrounded by friends and family who loved him
. . . and knew him.
His journals remain a testimony to the faithfulness of God
and to the importance of integrity and vulnerability
—even in the midst of our darkest moments
and despite the throbbing of our deepest pain.

Would you rather I had never opened up to you, remaining a stranger to you for the rest of my life? I don't think so. From my perspective, the closeness we've achieved has been worth the pain.

I realize now that it really isn't that important to live sixty or seventy years. Death is one of the only certainties in life. I honestly believe that how we live is more important than how long we live.

When it's my time to go, I'll be ready—God will see to that. And oh, with what joy will I embrace my advancement into Eternal Life, and a home with One who, though I've never seen, has always loved me best.

Scott Paul Cameron
Excerpt taken from the journal to his parents.

Afterwords

Therefore, confess your sins to one another,
and pray for one another,
so that you may be healed.
James 5:16

"LAUREN"

"Living a secret is hard. You don't remember what lies you've told; you inevitably close yourself off to everyone. But the risk of being vulnerable is hard, too. If you open up, what's going to happen? Will you be accepted? Or rejected?"

Lauren interrupts her thoughts with a sip of cinnamon iced tea. Three years after Scott's death, she's had time to mourn and evaluate and, yes, even learn. She sits in her small, quaint apartment about five miles from the Pacific Ocean. A cool breeze wafts through an open window behind her, rippling white lace curtains in sloping waves. Her strawberry-blonde hair hangs on her shoulders and a quiescent smile plays on her lips.

"Me, I'm a risk taker," she says. "I realize crisis prompts change. If Scott had allowed himself to be honest and vulnerable earlier in his struggle, sure, it may have seemed an excruciating crisis at the time – but maybe it could have changed him. I don't know for sure, but you need to believe that even in crisis, God's going to work it out. Even if people reject you, you're stronger because of your honesty. Being vulnerable may drive some people away. But it invites many loving, compassionate people to share your life and struggles. To me, that's worth the trade-off.

"Everybody has secret wounds and hurts deep inside. Some

people agonize over a broken relationship. I've got friends who have been betrayed or who are desperate with loneliness and isolation. Some people bear the scars of child abuse or even rape. Still others suffer because someone they love has died or is dying. These people are victims, but even victims can harbor secret aches that fester and bleed in the silence.

"For others, it's their own sin that gives birth to the secrets. Drug addiction, alcoholism, cheating, abortion, jealousy, back-stabbing—no one is worse than the next—they all erode our relationships and distance us from God. When we keep secrets, every area of our lives is impacted. The scars run deep, so deep. That's why honesty and vulnerability are so important.

"I'm convinced healing begins when things are revealed. It's no coincidence that alcohol recovery or any twelve-step program begins with a verbal admission of the problem. But we've got to take that first step. Transparency can mean risk; and some-times it means crisis. But it can mean wholeness, too, in the end."

"TAMMY"

A DC-10 roars into Long Beach Airport at 11:00 a.m. on a clear, brisk Southern California day. Just south of the airport on Lakewood Boulevard, past the Holiday Inn and Jack Webb Auto, sprawls a Spires restaurant.

Inside, beyond the Norman Rockwell prints and the plastic flora, sits a slim, diminutive girl. This is Tammy.

In the three years since her brother died, she has experi-enced it all: numbing grief, anger, relief, nostalgia, sorrow, res-ignation. The emotions still come in alternating waves.

"I'm mad at the whole stupid thing," she says, staring down at clenched hands. "Mad at what he did to himself; mad at what he did to us. He just never let on that anything was wrong, that he was struggling and suffering inside. All those years, all those vacations together . . . we never knew what he was going through.

"Scott never gave me a chance to be a real friend to him. I wanted to be. Growing up, we went to the same school, the same church, and had a lot of the same friends. But Scott kept me at a distance. He showed everybody one side—the happy, put-together side. He kept a lot hidden.

"Before he got sick, he pretty much lived his own life. On Christmas he would breeze in for a few hours, then go to work. He was in his apartment for three months before we got an invitation to go over.

"When he got sick, things didn't change right away. Gradually, he began to open up, to allow us into his life. He would call us up and say, 'Why don't you come on over?' That had never happened before. And when he was really sick, we used to sit with him and hold his hand. He read to us from his journal. Those were special times." The pitch of her voice drops with sadness.

"I guess he didn't think we would accept him and love him if he told us his secrets. He was wrong. We were raised to believe family is always there to help each other. He just didn't give us a chance—until the end, almost too late. We could have had a much deeper relationship—if we just could have just been honest."

"GAIL"

"A little while after Scott died, I got a phone call from a former principal I had worked with. No, not just worked with—we had become close friends before she moved up north. Anyway, I told her what had happened to Scott. Later that week I mailed her a copy of a magazine article about Scott. That was it. We've never heard from her since.

"Then there was a youth pastor from Scott's junior high days. Chuck and I wrote him a letter, telling him about Scott's death, and sent him a copy of the magazine article as well. We never heard from him. Never heard a word.

"It seems to me that the church has made one sin bigger than another, and I don't think it really is in the Lord's sight. With gay people, the church not only condemns them, but openly makes fun of them, creating an environment that isn't conducive to being vulnerable. And when you make yourself vulnerable—when you are honest—there are friends who don't know how to respond. Some are judgmental. Others just withdraw.

"Yet Chuck and I have received something precious from the whole heartbreak. Something like this just softens your heart to every need: you realize everybody has problems, you just don't know what they are.

"One time I had a neighbor whose husband had been out of work for a while. Chuck and I had given them a little bit of money and thought they were doing okay. Then one day my neighbor made the comment that they'd gotten sick from eating dog food. I was shocked. We would have gladly helped this family more—but we never knew how bad it was.

"We're all so proud; we're so afraid of being put down. For some reason, we've been led to believe that if we're really living right before the Lord, we won't have all these problems. But it just isn't so.

"It's my prayer—and Chuck's—that we could all just learn to share with each other without being so afraid that everyone else is perfect and won't accept our weaknesses."

"TONY"

"Not too long before Scott died, Caroline and I started having serious problems in our marriage." Tony, sitting on a avocado-green couch in a wood-paneled living room, talks about his personal struggles with a deliberation that implies a level of resolution as well as a bevy of painful memories. "Caroline and I separated and left our church while we tried to work out our problems.

"Before long, an elder in the church called me up to inform me I was officially cut off from fellowship. He said he was following Matthew 18, where it says to confront, in love, any Christian who is sinning. If that person doesn't repent, enlist the help of another believer for a second confrontation. If there still is no repentance, take the matter before the local church, and separate the unrepentant believer from fellowship. The elder from my church said he was obeying Matthew 18—but he skipped steps one and two.

"The thing is, no one even asked *why* we were getting divorced. No one ever tried to counsel us through it. I felt betrayed; I felt abandoned. But I also felt a sense of irony, of poetic justice: This was, after all, not unlike the way I was told to handle Scott when the news broke at church that he was gay."

Tony had been in the epicenter during those turbulent times in Scott's life, and now, years later, his misgivings and regrets are evident despite the fact that he and Scott reconciled their relationship.

"Scott got involved in an issue that's morally and politically volatile, both for the church and society. Homosexuality is that kind of issue. So is abortion. I'm convinced that issues like that polarize people, leaving little middle ground. The opposition becomes easy for Christians to target, and the result is an us-versus-them mentality: Someone tells us how we as Christians are supposed to react as a group, and we follow. There's little room for individual thinking, because anyone who ventures beyond the appropriate behavior for his or her group is suddenly suspect: People begin to wonder, 'Is he one of them?'

"Polarization lessens the church's sensitivity toward the person involved. We can't respond with any degree of personal vulnerability or concern, because we're too caught up with giving the appropriate group response. And we can't minister to the individual hurts and needs of the person we're confronting, because we don't see a fallen man or woman not unlike ourselves—we see a stereotype.

"I thought I was doing the right thing, extricating myself from Scott. But I know now that those of us who confronted Scott were long on truth, short on love. You know, the first priority of Matthew 18 is the protection of the person in sin. The whole passage starts: 'If he listens to you, you win your brother.' The goal is to restore him, not degrade him."

"CHARLES"

"Ten years! Ten years I lived a lie to my family and friends. I was involved in the gay lifestyle for ten years, but I couldn't tell them how I felt or what I was struggling with. I was afraid I'd be abandoned, excommunicated."

Charles slouches in a brown-leather chair in a windowless office. He met Scott in the AIDS support group that both men attended. Charles had been out of the gay lifestyle for five years when he tested positive for AIDS. It's true that he survived Scott Cameron, but Charles knows it's just a matter of time. He was recently diagnosed with cancer.

"Finally—*finally*—I opened my mouth and told a few Christian friends what I was involved in, what I battled with. And that was the turning point for me. That's what got me on the right path. A load of bricks dropped from my shoulders, and for the first time in ten years, I knew I could beat this thing.

"You know, there's power when things are revealed.

"Just me and God hadn't been enough. Certainly not because God wasn't powerful enough, but because I needed the help of Christian friends to carry me through. God used those people as an extension of Himself to give me the strength I needed to fight off waves of temptation and self-doubt.

"There were many times I felt tempted and called up Christian friends for support. We hit our knees and didn't get up till the old desires were gone. Sometimes that would be an hour. Sometimes more. Even so, change didn't happen overnight. I've been out of the lifestyle for seven years now, and I still get waves of temptation. That's when I grab a friend and we hit our knees in prayer. Accountability, you know? It's not magic, but it works. Thank God it works."

"GARY"

As we put the finishing touches on this book, Gary is dying as a result of AIDS. He is undergoing chemotherapy to combat a form of lymphoma, although the doctors say his cancer is not responding to the treatment. He was recently diagnosed with a second form of cancer, Kaposi's Sarcoma—the same cancer that caused Scott's death. Gary is not expected to live more than a few weeks.

Despite the encouragement of Tammy, Lauren, Gail, Chuck, and others, Gary has so far refused the invitation to a personal relationship with Jesus Christ.

FOR A FREE CATALOG OF
NAVPRESS BOOKS & BIBLE STUDIES,
CALL TOLL FREE 800-366-7788 (USA)
or 1-416-499-4615 (CANADA)